BY APPOINTMENT
TO HM THE QUEEN
MANUFACTURERS OF ROVER CARS
LAND ROVERS AND RANGE ROVERS
ROVER GROUP LTD. COVENTRY

BY APPOINTMENT
TO HRH THE DUKE OF EDINBURGH
MANUFACTURERS OF
LAND ROVERS AND RANGE ROVERS
ROVER GROUP LTD. COVENTRY

BY APPOINTMENT
TO HRH THE PRINCE OF WALES
MANUFACTURERS OF
LAND ROVERS AND RANGE ROVERS
ROVER GROUP LTD, COVENTRY

Working in the Wild
Land Rover's
Manual for Africa

Revised Edition
2nd Revised Edition January 2008

Land Rover Headquarters,
Warwick Technology Park, Warwick,
Warwickshire, CV34 6RG UK.
Telephone: 44 (0) 1926 482020
www.Landrover.com
20/02Z8-1935

Printed in England

WORKING IN THE WILD - LAND ROVER'S MANUAL FOR AFRICA

HOW TO USE THIS MANUAL

The 'Working in the Wild' handbook has been designed to be just as useful in an emergency as it is for someone making careful forward plans.

The **KEY QUESTIONS** Section is designed to help the reader find his or her way around the handbook quickly and easily.

The **IN-DEPTH** Sections are the second part of most chapters. They cover each subject in full but remain concise and uncomplicated. The information is clear and easy to put into practice.

SECTION SEVEN is a general information section which includes guidance and advice on living and working in hot countries as well as useful information on communications and conversion tables.

REFERENCE ONLY: The Key questions also act as an index and are supported by a full alphabetical cross-reference section at the end of Section Seven.

All **CROSS REFERENCES** in the text use section numbers: i.e. 7.A = Part A of Section 7.

PAGE NUMBERING: A two-figure system (Page 2-1 = 1st page of Section 2) has been used to allow for future updates.

Fritz Curzon

BUCKINGHAM PALACE

Many of my overseas visits as President of Save the Children Fund have confirmed the vital importance of efficient transport in the operations that voluntary organisations undertake: everything from making sure that vaccines reach immunisation centres on time, to setting up and maintaining a vehicle fleet for grain distribution to famine hit areas.

Conditions are often inhospitable, so I welcome this manual by two Land Rover engineers which aims to help users keep their Land Rovers running efficiently "virtually anywhere on Earth". The authors have drawn on many people's experience, as well as their own secondments to Oxfam during the famine in Western Sudan, to produce a book with the emphasis on practical know-how where it matters most – at fieldwork level!

Let us hope that it will prove a giant step in defeating the "too many moving parts" syndrome which seems to afflict so many of our best efforts.

Anne

LAND ROVER

Lode Lane, Solihull
West Midlands B92 8NW
England

Telephone: 021 722 2424
International: +4421 722 2424
Telex: 338641 LanRov G
Fax: 021 742 1927

Land Rovers are used as workhorses all over the world - and nowhere do they have a harder job to do than in Africa.

Two Land Rover engineers who worked in the Sudan saw a pressing need for ready made answers to the questions posed by customers and users who face difficult and arduous operating conditions in the field.

The result is "Working in the Wild", a book designed to bridge the gap between the Land Rover handbook and the Workshop Manual.

Though no single book could possibly cover the range of conditions, situations and problems encountered around the world, this one comes close.

The enthusiasm of the authors for the project ensured that it won the support of many experienced people within Land Rover and outside, all of whom we would like to thank for their invaluable co-operation and contributions.

I hope this book helps you to get the most out of your Land Rover, wherever you use it.

C J S WOODWARK
COMMERCIAL DIRECTOR - LAND ROVER

INTRODUCTION

Working In the Wild - Land Rover's Manual for Africa bridges the gap that exists between conventional motor manuals and expedition handbooks.

It has been produced to assist anyone for whom Land Rover Defenders are a means of survival rather than simply a method of transport.

Unlike most manuals issued by manufacturers, it goes well beyond the workshop engineering details: it tackles the whole business of managing, deploying, maintaining and even driving the vehicle to maximum effect.

It pulls together the practical experience of dozens of people who know and understand the dangers, challenges, difficulties and pitfalls encountered in hostile territories.

The revised edition draws upon over 50 years worth of knowledge of the Land Rover to show how the vehicle's unique qualities can be applied in extreme conditions.

It is designed for use both as a quick reference handbook for individuals and as a management manual for the operation of a single Defender or an entire fleet of vehicles.

Working In the Wild - Land Rover's Manual for Africa makes available a fund of practical knowledge which will help people working individually or as part of a team anywhere in the world.

The book will be vital for anyone for whom difficult operating conditions are or will be a way of life.

INTRODUCTION TO THE REVISED EDITION

Like all products that consistently lead in their fields, Land Rovers have continued to evolve, and whilst the general body shape and the world beating coil suspension of 110's and 90's remains as we have always known them, a host of other changes have arrived.

Some might be described as just cosmetic; what was a "Land Rover" for over 40 years, became a "Defender" in September 1990. But other changes are more important, like the outstanding new engines variously fitted since 1990; the diesel TDI's.

First the 200TDI series in September 1990, then the 300TDI in April 1994, and the radical newest incarnation, the TD5 in September 1998, that has brought electronic engine management into the vehicle.

There have been changes too to the way things are in Africa, and it is now more important than ever for the traveller or long-term operator to be well prepared and properly equipped for field maintenance.

All of this has led to this revised edition of "Working in the Wild". It remains one of the best reference sources for anyone needing to operate and maintain a Land Rover in Africa, whether as a long-term fleet manager, or as a private owner, on secondment or on safari.

There is an entirely new section on the subject of tyres; how to understand the way they are described, and how to begin a choice of what might best suit your needs. And there are new tips on how to nip potential problems in the bud, and how to get yourself (and your vehicle) home when things look really difficult.

There is also (but only) a brief section on the TD5 engine.

A few of words of caution, however. It is never possible to cover every combination of "what if". At the end of the day, working in the wild with any vehicle can mean a situation which requires repair beyond what can be done "out there".

This is particularly relevant to the TD5. Its sophisticated electronic management system includes a "get you home" programme that automatically engages in the event of a major system failure. This keeps the engine running at a specific speed and enables slow but sure progress. However, the nature of electronics is such that very little can be done by way of field maintenance without powerful computers and the relevant programmes. It is also possible for the entire electronic management system to go down, including the "get you home" feature, if the ECU is introduced to water.

Finally, a word about the other Land Rover that has become very much a field companion to the Defender - the Discovery. It's mechanicals and their maintenance have a great deal that is common to the Defender. Therefore, much of this manual is relevant to the Discovery too.

However, the manual remains firstly specific to "Defenders", and in order to avoid confusion, the name "Defender" is used throughout to apply to the coil sprung vehicles that were once before just called Land Rovers. But don't worry if you have an older model that is not badged "Defender"; the data and guidance that pertain to the earlier vehicles - petrol and diesel - is retained.

And above all, they remain superbly tough and long lasting vehicles.

CHRISTOPHER RACE

Africa Insight (Pty) Ltd.   November 2002

1. WHICH DEFENDER? - Selecting the right model for the job.

Vehicle options - Choosing a dealer - The importance of pre-delivery inspections - Warranties - Optional Equipment - Accessories - Tyres

2. WHAT SPARES? - Compiling and maintaining a stock of parts.

Purchasing - Designing a Kit - Making Parts lists - Careful Packing - Correct Ordering - Sale Storage

3. WHO DRIVES? - The partnership between vehicle and driver.

Driver training in UK and abroad - Vehicle management - Keeping log books - Routine checks - Correct loading - Care for the Environment - Driving Off-Road - Safe Winching - Driving Procedures - Guide Charts - Emergency Action - Improvised Repairs

4. WHAT FUEL? - Vital steps to ensure quality.

Fuel Facts - Typical consumption - Buying, storing and pumping - Keeping fuel clean - Drum stores - Quality tests - Diesel storage

5. WHICH WORKSHOP? - Planning a maintenance programme.

Designing and building a workshop; location, equipment, personnel, administration - Advice on pit construction - Vehicle and workshop tool kits - Sample administration cards - Simple service schedule

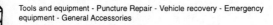

6. WHICH EXTRAS? - Selecting the right accessories.

Tools and equipment - Puncture Repair - Vehicle recovery - Emergency equipment - General Accessories

7. WHAT IF. . .? - Wide-ranging and useful information.

Phonetic alphabet - International Ground Air distress code - World maximum ambient temperature zones - High ambients - Solar load - Effects of altitude - Humidity - Human water needs - Fire fighting - Weights and measures - Densities - Temperature conversion - Land Rover Publications - Recommended independent publications

Alphabetical index and author's acknowledgements.

1. WHICH DEFENDER?

1. WHICH DEFENDER?

How to make sure you have the right Defender for the job. This section profiles, compares and contrasts the basic choices of power and chassis options for types of terrain and tasks.

The 'Which Defender?' section also advises on who to buy Land Rovers from and what you can expect from the three types of recommended outlet. It examines the key issue of service support and how to structure and establish a dependable servicing routine.

CONTENTS

B. **Body**

1. Rear Seats for Utility models
2. Rear side windows for Hard Top models (Sliding or fixed)
3. Trim options. Sound/heat Insulation
4. Trim options. Vinyl or cloth seats.
5. Air Conditioning
6. Hoods for Pickups with or without windows
7. Steps - side and rear
8. Front Mud flaps

C. **Chassis**

1. 90 High Load suspension kit
2. Heavy Duty wheels, second spares and spare wheel covers
3. Steering Protection Kit - Drag Link and Track Rod
4. Towing Kits - Pintles - 50mm Ball - Hook and Height Adjustable

D. **Electrical**

1. Heavy Duty alternator (65A)
2. Batteries - Heavy Duty or Extra Heavy Duty + spares wet or dry charged
3. Split-Charge Facility
4. Radio Preparation + Additional Gauges
5. Rear wash/wipe kit
6. Fire extinguisher

E.   Accessories

1. Roof Racks + roof ladders
2. Winches and ground anchors
3. Bull Bars
4. Power Take Offs - centre and rear
5. Lights - additional + protection
6. Audio Equipment
7. Load bay protection
8. Extra heavy-duty mats
9. Dog guards + gun clips
10. Warning Triangles
11. Alarm Systems
12. Tyre Chains

1.H   Selecting the Right Tyres

Your tyres must be considered as an integral part of your vehicle's overall specification. This section shows how to match conditions with tyres designed to cope with them; On-road/Off-road/Dual purpose; Mud, Snow, Sand; Use of Tyre Chains; Tyre Pressures. It also tells you how to understand sizing.

1.I   Land Rover Worldwide Distributors

Information on Land Rover distribution with addresses and web-sites for the UK and Southern Africa.

1.J   Land Rover Export Dealers

Land Rovers export organisation who can advise on and supply vehicles, additional equipment, spares packs and warranty information on vehicles for Africa and the Gulf states.

Whatever you do and wherever your work takes you, there is a Land Rover Defender to help you carry it out more effectively.

Hundreds of vehicle and equipment options have evolved from Land Rover's first-hand experience in more than 160 countries since 1948. The company's 4 x 4 vehicles are designed and built to cope with virtually every kind of terrain and environmental condition on Earth.

Land Rover Defenders are built to withstand high and low temperatures, altitudes and humidity levels. They can be built to overcome individual operating problems like contaminated or even watered fuel.

To make the most of the experience which lies behind every Land Rover and to ensure that you have the right Land Rover Defender for the job, please call our sales department at Solihull for free territorial specification advice.

1.B VEHICLE CHOICE - WHICH LAND ROVER FOR THE JOB?

1. WHY A LAND ROVER?

The first Land Rover grew out of a need for a tough, reliable, easily-maintained and long-lasting working vehicle.

Though the familiar square-shouldered silhouette of the Land Rover Defender remains, hundreds of major and minor improvements over the years have enabled the vehicle to evolve in line with technical advances and the needs of people all over the world.

Land Rover's new 5-cylinder turbo charged diesel introduces state of the art engine management technology to the modern Defenders. It features 'common rail' fuel injection and completely electronic engine management, enabling optimum power delivery with exceptionally low exhaust emissions. However, this engine requires specialised maintenance equipment and training.

For operations in remote areas of Africa, the 300TDI engine remains an available option.

2. WHAT MAKES THE LAND ROVER SO EFFECTIVE?

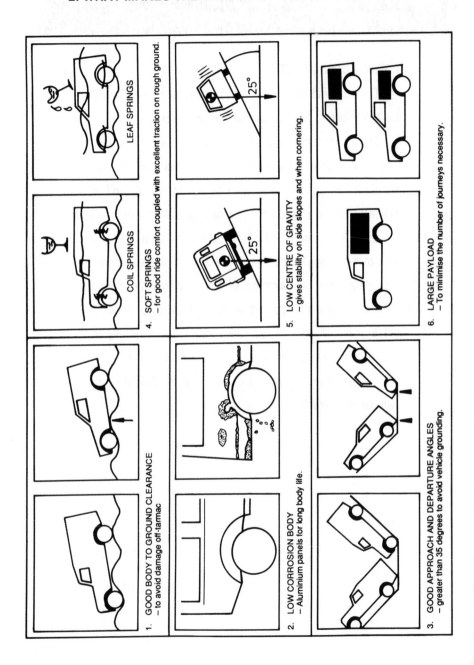

1. GOOD BODY TO GROUND CLEARANCE
   – to avoid damage off-tarmac

2. LOW CORROSION BODY
   – Aluminium panels for long body life.

3. GOOD APPROACH AND DEPARTURE ANGLES
   – greater than 35 degrees to avoid vehicle grounding.

4. SOFT SPRINGS
   – for good ride comfort coupled with excellent traction on rough ground.

LEAF SPRINGS

COIL SPRINGS

5. LOW CENTRE OF GRAVITY
   – gives stability on side slopes and when cornering.

6. LARGE PAYLOAD
   – To minimise the number of journeys necessary.

25°

25°

3. THE RANGE OF CHOICES

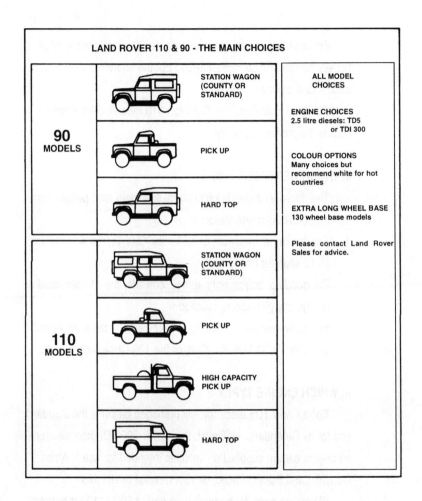

LAND ROVER 110 & 90 - THE MAIN CHOICES

90 MODELS

- STATION WAGON (COUNTY OR STANDARD)
- PICK UP
- HARD TOP

110 MODELS

- STATION WAGON (COUNTY OR STANDARD)
- PICK UP
- HIGH CAPACITY PICK UP
- HARD TOP

ALL MODEL CHOICES

ENGINE CHOICES
2.5 litre diesels: TD5 or TDI 300

COLOUR OPTIONS
Many choices but recommend white for hot countries

EXTRA LONG WHEEL BASE
130 wheel base models

Please contact Land Rover Sales for advice.

Information on the complete range of Land Rover factory fitted options and accessories is in Section 1.G

For mobility: The shorter wheelbase 90 models are exceptionally nimble and tractable off-road but the shorter overall length means less payload.

For load carrying: The Defender 110 models offer almost double the payload capacity.

4. WHICH DEFENDER 110?

The decision depends on the vehicle's main role: people carrying or goods/equipment transport:

1. For personnel transport, consider the One Ten Station Wagon (9-12 seats or goods).
2. For goods or equipment haulage, consider the 110 standard or hi-capacity pick-ups or Hardtop.
3. For a combination of seating capacity and hi-cap load, consider either the 110 Double Cab, or the 130 Crew Cab models.

5. WHICH ENGINE TYPE?

The all new TD5 electronically managed diesel is the standard unit for all Defenders. However, the earlier 300 TDI (non electronic) engine can be supplied on vehicles intended for use in Africa. Consult Land Rover Limited, or your nearest dealership.

(If you are considering buying an earlier 90 or 110 for remote areas, the golden rule is: Keep it simple. Earlier engine options included 4-cylinder and V8 petrol units. As a rule of thumb, petrol engined vehicles are less expensive to purchase, but use more fuel than diesels. Also, petrol is difficult to store safely and more volatile than diesel. See Section 4.B for comparison information to help your decision).

6. Extra equipment options for Defenders

TYRE CHOICES
This is not a simple-choice exercise and no tyre is the only "right" option. It's always going to involve compromise. See tyre guide Section 1.H.

REAR LIGHT PROTECTION
Keeps your lights working when operating in rough conditions.

TOWING PINTLE
Strong, secure point for towing-rope attachment when recovering vehicles off-tarmac.

ADDITIONAL FUEL TANK & SEDIMENTORS
Additional tankage increases range (an essential requirement where fuel supplies are scarce), and is an easier handling option than cans. Sedimentors provide additional filtering to cope with dirty or watered fuel.

ROOF RACK
Very useful when travelling on 'expedition'. Beware of over-loading rack. See Section 3.G.

RAISED AIR INTAKE
Increases air filter life under dusty conditions. Avoids possibility of engine damage when wading deep water.

UNDERSIDE PROTECTION BAR
Protection to steering gear from natures obstacles.

SECOND SPARE WHEEL
Lockable bonnet mounted spare - essential when terrain results in daily punctures.

FRONT LIGHT GUARDS
Essential to protect headlights from branch damage. No lights - no night driving.

CHAFF GUARD
Avoids difficult radiator-out cleaning, after driving through tall grass.

WINCH
A great advantage in certain self-recovery situations (especially solo). Options include either hydraulic or electric powered units. Electric winches allow limited operation when the vehicle engine is not running; hydraulic winches require the engine to be running, but can be operated continuously for very long periods.

Land Rovers can be bought from countless sources in countries all over the world. But, unless your organisation has negotiated special purchasing rights with Land Rover, we can recommend only three ways of buying one:

1.   THE IN-TERRITORY DISTRIBUTOR NETWORK

The distributor closest to the region in which your vehicle will be operated can use his practical experience to advise you on specification choice.

He will take care of your vehicle's importation and will ensure that it is in good order on delivery. He will look after your vehicle under warranty for a full year from the day you take delivery from him.

2.   LAND ROVER EXPORT

Land Rover Export is a part of Land Rover and which was set up specifically to deal with the needs of export customers.

Trained staff based in London, Dubai and Land Rover South Africa have extensive practical experience of the vehicles, the climates and terrains of overseas territories and the legal requirements for operating vehicles in individual regions. See section 1.l

3. **The UK Based Export Distributor Network**

Land Rover approved UK based Export Distributor, whose product knowledge, field experience and export facilities meet exacting standards. They offer warranty support and spares supply from the UK.

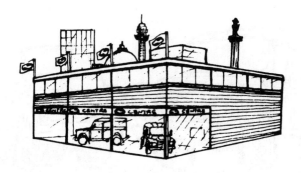

REMEMBER - If you decide to buy your Land Rover from a non- recommended source, wrong advice on the choice of vehicle in relation to terrain/climatic/legal conditions may affect warranty cover. (See warranty conditions, Section 1.F and Vehicle Handbook).

THE PRE-DELIVERY INSPECTION (PDI)

Under no circumstances should the PDI be regarded as a mere rubber-stamping exercise for time-wasting bureaucrats.

It is an essential part of the process which will ensure a long, effective life for a Land Rover.

Insist on a full all-points inspection and insist that it is carried out by a Land Rover qualified mechanic.

1.E PREVENTATIVE MAINTENANCE

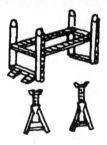 Land Rover Defenders are designed to last a working lifetime - many of their predecessors are still going strong after 50 years hard labour.

Today's Defender continues to offer this possibility of service, but it can't do it alone.

1. THE FIRST SERVICE

The most important of your Defenders working life - and is free of labour parts charges (except for oil and sundries - See your handbook). It is usually carried out by an approved dealer at 1500 Kms or 1000 miles.

Should your location make it difficult to ensure the job is done by an approved distributor, make alternative arrangements with your vendor. A few simple but important checks and adjustments made now can influence your Defenders performance in years to come.

2. SERVICE INTERVALS IN REMOTE AREAS

The demanding terrain, high temperatures (greater than 40°C) and penetrating dust often found in developing countries mean that service intervals should be no more than 4000 Kms (2500 miles) or two months apart, whichever is sooner.

In some cases, servicing may need to be more frequent still. Check with a Land Rover approved distributor or an operator with practical local experience.

REMEMBER. The responsibility for maintenance is yours from the moment you collect your vehicle. You can't depend on reminders.

1.F WARRANTY - IF A PART FAILS, CAN IT BE REPLACED FREE?

Components that prove to have a material or manufacturing defect within 12 months or 20,000 Kms (12,000 miles) after the date of purchase from factory or dealer will be replaced free of charge.

REMEMBER. Keep your service record book complete and up to date and always present it for validation at each service. Record all service activity even if this is not carried out by an approved dealer.

Glass and tyres are expressly excluded from warranty claims, but manufacturers of tyres fitted as standard to Land Rover vehicles will always be prepared to consider genuine claims.

Fair wear and tear, lack of maintenance or unapproved alterations will be taken into consideration with respect to claims. Full warranty details can be found in the workshop maintenance section of the owner's handbook. Warranty work is normally carried out by approved dealers. Warranties start from the day of purchase - so the closer your vendor to the vehicle's destination the better.

WARRANTY CLAIMS FROM REMOTE AREAS

The return of faulty parts from remote areas may be difficult so the following steps should be taken.

A. In-Territory Distributor - if you bought the vehicle from them or registered the vehicle from them on arrival, they will deal with your warranty claims.

B. Land Rover Export Ltd - this company will arrange warranties on vehicles it sells, either with an in-territory distributor or with a UK based export distributor.

C. UK based Export Distributor - warranty claims dealt with direct unless arrangements made with local distributor.

D. If none of the above, file a warranty claim with your vendor, along with evidence in support of your claim:

i) Your Defender's Vehicle Identification Number (VIN) (see handbook for location of number).

ii) Type of Defender and miles covered: e.g. 110 Station Wagon TD5, Left Hand Steering, 10,503 Kms.

iii) Official Land Rover part number and description of faulty component(s) - check with parts catalogue if at all possible.

iv) Brief account of local conditions: e.g. typical ambients 40°C, high dust levels, 60 per cent driving on rough tracks - remainder cross country.

v) Photographs of faulty component(s) and/or circumstances surrounding its failure. e.g. component failed when vehicle on rough track.

vi) Date and source of purchase of vehicle. e.g. May 2002 from Land Rover Export Ltd.

vii) Date service in destination country began. e.g. June 2002 Ethiopia.

Land Rover Export Ltd or your approved Land Rover Distributor will advise on up-to-date information on options and accessories.

REMEMBER - it is not possible to fit all options on a single vehicle. Consult Land Rover Export or Distributor when planning your equipment and accessories.

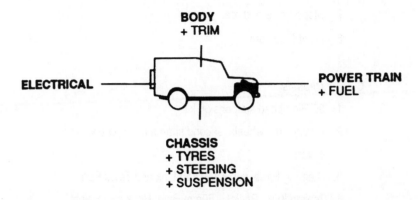

BODY + TRIM

ELECTRICAL

POWER TRAIN + FUEL

CHASSIS + TYRES + STEERING + SUSPENSION

Factory Fitted Options

A. *Power train*

1. Raised air intake
2. Chaff guard
3. Additional fuel tanks
4. Extra fuel sedimentors
5. Hand throttles

B. **Body**

1. Rear seats for Utility models

2. Rear side windows for Hard Top models (Sliding or fixed)

3. Trim options. Sound/heat insulation

4. Trim options. Vinyl or cloth seats.

5. Air Conditioning

6. Hoods for Pickups with or without windows

7. Steps - side and rear

8. Front Mud flaps

C. **Chassis**

1. 90 High Load suspension kit

2. Heavy Duty wheels, second spares and spare wheel covers

3. Steering Protection Kit - Drag Link and Track Rod

4. Towing Kits - Pintles - 50mm Ball - Hook and Height Adjustable

D. **Electrical**

1. Heavy Duty alternator (65A)

2. Batteries- Heavy Duty or Extra Heavy Duty + spares wet or dry charged

3. Split-Charge Facility

4. Radio Preparation + Additional Gauges

5. Rear wash/wipe kit

6. Fire extinguisher

E. *Accessories*

1. Roof Racks + roof ladders
2. Winches and ground anchors
3. Bull Bars
4. Power Take Offs - centre and rear
5. Lights - additional + protection
6. Audio Equipment
7. Load bay protection
8. Extra heavy-duty mats
9. Dog guards + gun clips
10. Warning Triangles
11. Alarm Systems
12. Tyre Chains

LAND ROVER OPTIONS YOU SHOULD CONSIDER . . .

A. *The Power train*

1. *Raised air intakes: High dust levels and deep water wading*

Defenders which may be used for deep water crossings and in arid areas where high dust levels will be created can be specified with an external roof-level high performance air intake assembly. (Cyclonic pre-cleaners)

The no-maintenance systems are essential for river crossings greater than 20". (500mm) deep in which even minor waves of water into the standard air intake could cause major engine damage - particularly to Diesels.

2. Chaff guard radiator protector

The wind-blown build-up of grass seeds or chaff in the fine mesh of a cooling radiator can cause a creeping rise in engine temperature. The Chaff Guard filters the potentially damaging seeds and can be brushed clean easily without removal.

3. Additional fuel tanks

Without loss of ground clearance but at the expense of payload capacity, up to 85 per cent extra range can be achieved with extra tanks. An extra tank can be fitted and is easily switched by the driver who can use a central fuel gauge for monitoring all tanks.

4. Extra fuel sedimentors: For dirty watered diesel

A valuable option for diesel Defenders which will operate in areas where dirty and water-contaminated fuel may be all that is available.

The Sedimentor is a reusable automatic centrifugal system built into the vehicle's fuel system to 'spin out' impurities from the fuel before it is injected into the engine. It requires regular cleaning.

5. Hand throttles: Pto and winches

For fingertip control of engine speed during a Land Rover's operation as a static power source for winches and other equipment. The dashboard-mounted control can be set in one of several engine speed rates.

B   The Body

1.   Side-facing rear seats: Simple seating for utility models

For tasks in which personnel carrying may be involved, this option retains the full interior length space for goods and equipment.

2.   Rear windows for hard tops

For improved visibility to rear, simple 'fixed' or sliding windows may be specified. (This may affect vehicle tax status in certain markets).

3.   Trim options: Sound/heat Insulation

Specially formulated floor covering and roof headlining combination cuts road noise at high speed and reduces ambient temperature inside vehicle under high tropical solar load.

4.   Trim options: Cool seating

For increased comfort in hot countries, cloth seats can be specified.

5.   Air conditioning: For hot environment

A high degree of control over internal temperature in extreme conditions of heat and work is possible with the optional built-in air conditioning unit. These require special service parts so likely availability in destination territory should be checked in advance.

6. Hoods for pickups: Load protection

Quickly detachable waterproof canvas hoods which cover the full-length load space of Defender pick-ups to protect loads from sun and rain are available. The galvanised steel-tube framed hoods can feature side windows.

7. Steps - Side and rear

All side and rear doors can be equipped with chassis-mounted foldaway steps.

8. Front mud flaps: Under body protection

Together with the standard fitment rear mud flaps, the optional front flaps protect the vehicles underbelly from damage by debris thrown up by the front wheels.

C The Chassis

1. High load suspension: 90 models extra load

For extra load carrying capacity of 150 kg over the maximum recommended for Land Rovers equipped with standard single rate coil springs, dual rate springs can be fitted without loss of ride comfort. The option includes the fitting of a higher-specification differential.

2. Heavy Duty Wheels & Tyres

Tyre choice is very important so a full section is included in section 1.H.

A second bonnet-mounted spare wheel can be fitted for

regions where tyre damage and punctures are likely. Extra under-bonnet bracing is used to support the mounting bracket. Tyre covers are also available.

Wider, heavy duty ventilated wheels can be specified at time of purchase of new Defenders. They may also be retro-fitted to all models; however when this is done, new, longer wheel studs must be fitted on all hubs. ONLY Land Rover specification wheels should be fitted; serious failure could occur if this is not done.

3. Steering protection kit: Arduous off-road use

A chassis-mounted energy absorbing bar can be fitted below the front bumper to protect the drag-link in rough off-road use. Extra challenging conditions can be met with a thick aluminium plate guard. (Illustrated in Section 6.F)

4. Towing kits: On and off-road use

The Land Rover can be equipped to undertake virtually all towing permutations. Direct chassis cross-member mounted hook or pintle for off-road trailers or recovery work.

For on-road trailers a 50mm ball, hook or pintle system can be attached to an additional lower chassis-mounted bracket. An adjustable towing bar kit for various draw bar heights is also available.

D. Electrical

1. Heavy-duty alternator: For high load accessories

A 65 amp alternator replaces the standard 45 amp version, to produce 44 per cent more power output for high current extras - electrical winches, spotlights, refrigeration units. (65 amp alternator is standard on air conditioned and split-charge equipped vehicles).

2. Heavy-duty batteries: Extra power for starting or powering accessories

Recommended when operating the vehicle in cold areas or for coping with increased load of high current accessories - a winch etc. (For earlier petrol engined Defenders, 42 per cent more capacity can be obtained by replacing the standard 55 amp. hour battery with the available 78 amp. hour heavy duty).

The standard 78 amp. hour batteries fitted to Diesel engined Defenders can be replaced with an extra heavy duty 93 amp. hour battery with 20 per cent more capacity. Additional batteries - either 'dry' for long term storage or 'wet' for earlier use - can be supplied with export vehicles.

3. Split-charge facility: Charging system for extra battery

Second batteries must be linked to the charging circuit, using a voltage sensing switch and relay. This control unit ensures that the main battery is priority charged and that no mutual discharging between the batteries can occur, e.g. If an electrical accessory is accidentally left switched on, only the second battery will drain. Defenders equipped in this way are fitted with 65 amp alternators.

4. Radio preparation + Additional gauges

Your new Defender can be equipped with an optional radio fitting kit for the radio of your choice. The fitted kit includes two speakers, aerial, fused power leads and dashboard fittings. For security reasons, radios are not fitted to export vehicles. For battery condition checks, a voltmeter can be fitted.

5. Rear Wash/wipe kit: For Improved rear visibility

A system for keeping clear rearward visibility in muddy, wet or dusty conditions. A double washer jet powered by an under-bonnet pump sprays water onto the rear screen and a door-fitted wiper blade clears it.

6. Fire extinguisher: For safety

Always carry a fire extinguisher. Land Rover Supplies BCF, extinguishers in 1 kg and 1.5 kg sizes.

E   Accessories

All accessories listed in Section 1.G are available from Land Rover Parts through Land Rover dealers and distributors. Fleet buyers can specify factory fitment of accessories. Contact your dealer for the latest information.

1.H CHOOSING THE RIGHT TYRES

No tyre is perfect for all driving conditions. Knowing what kind of conditions to expect will, however, enable you to select from the wide range of options available.

The information given in this section has been drawn from the collective experience of Land Rover people driving the vehicle in many countries around the world.

The advice is based on a consensus of personal views and opinions rather than the findings of scientific research and is offered to you in that spirit.

For this reason, we cannot be held responsible for any events or circumstances arising from use or misuse of the information.

1. Making sense of sizes

All Defender 110's are fitted with 750R16 tyres as standard equipment; Defender 90's can have either this size, or the smaller 600R16. The equivalent Metric sizes are 265/75-16 and 205/75-16.

When fitting the larger size 750 or 265/75 to a Defender 90, ensure that the correct ratio gear drive for the speedometer is also fitted to the gearbox. (The standard 110 part is interchangeable). This will ensure that speed and distance readings remain accurate; distance recording is particularly important when travelling in Africa as fuel supplies can be far apart.

Understanding tyre sizes and dimensions is important, particularly when faced with products that are marked entirely differently to what you have on your vehicle. Nothing is more peculiar than the way tyres are sized; what exactly is a 7.50R16 or a 265/75R16?

Before the days of metrication, tyre dimensions were in Imperial measurements - inches. Defender 110's were fitted with 7.50R16's.

7.50 is the height of the sidewall in inches; in other words, 7.5 inches. This measurement includes the height of the bead of the tyre - the part that sits within the wheel rim.

But Imperial tyre size categories had no <u>width</u> measurement, and thus a 7.50R16 could be either narrow (like the Michelin XS) or wider (like the Turkish LASA).

The letter **R,** or the word 'Radial' indicate radial construction. If there is no such notation, the tyre will almost certainly be of cross-ply construction; that is, the weave of the plys goes across from side to side of the tyre. Radial and cross-ply tyres have very different characteristics and should not be mixed. (If in an absolute emergency there is no alternative to mixing, the cross plys must always be on the front).

The figure **16** is the size of the wheel rim (diameter), also in inches. With a few notable exceptions, all Land Rover Defenders (and their predecessors since 1948) have left the factory with 16-inch rims as standard on all models. **However**, there are different width rims, ranging from 6 to 8.5 inches. Many modern tyres cannot function effectively if fitted to narrow rims.

Today it is most common to find tyres sizes in Metric form - 265/75R16 for example. What do the figures mean?

Choosing the best tyre is a matter of compromise, and the modern range of radials offers an extensive range of choice. Here are examples of some of the best tread profiles for African conditions. All are suitable for the whole Defender range.

Michelin XZL fitted to a Defender 130. An excellent dual purpose on/off road tyre with good mileage potential on tarmac.

Australian manufactured Dunlop Super Gripper. Wide tread face and an amazing off road tyre; one of the best options available for all round African conditions. Noisy on tar.

R indicates 'radial construction, and the 16 denotes the size of the rim to be used - still calculated in inches!

265 is the overall <u>width</u> of the tyre measured in millimetres (that's the metric bit).

75 is the height of the tyre, <u>shown as a percentage of the width.</u> (If the percentage measure for height is 45 or less, the tyre is classed as 'low profile'. Fitting low profile tyres enables larger diameter rims to be used without increasing the overall rolling radius (circumference) of the tyre.

Knowing how to interpret these dimensions means one can easily calculate whether a replacement tyre is of compatible size to the others on a vehicle. Tyres with widely different rolling radii must not be fitted together.

2. What about width?

Wide may look macho, but its not always functional; a wide footprint increases on-road fuel consumption and may not always provide the best off-road grip.

It's important to remember that both diameter and width con-tribute to flotation - that is the extent to which a tyre 'floats' rather than sinks, into loose surfaces.

When selecting a wide tyre for general use - and especially for dry sand - look for side lugs. These are buttress-like treads that

Michelin XS, the all time benchmark tyre for sand, even when worn as much as this. Noisy and inclined to wear on tar, but nevertheless good. The XS is a "tall" tyre with larger rolling radius than most 7.50R's; for this reason, should not be mixed. Gives a significant increase in ground clearance.

Continental Conti Trac, another hard wearing excellent all rounder with wide profile. This example has had six years, mostly on-road, service.

stand out, and can be quite small. The key thing is that they must be there; they dig and grip on loose surfaces like hot desert sand. Lug-less tyres in such conditions can very dramatically affect fuel consumption and mobility.

In contrast, beach conditions, or continuous water-logged sand favour lug-less tyres.

3. Tubes or tubeless?

In most parts of Africa - including many cities - it is not possible to have punctured tubeless tyres repaired.

It is also common to have significant sized holes pierced through tyres, which will then require an inner gaiter to be fitted.

Damage to rim edges is also common, and this too can prevent the sealing of a tubeless tyre.

It may therefore be unwise to equip with tubeless tyres, although they are superior to tubed tyres in many respects.

However, it is always essential to carry heavy duty tubes as spares, as well as a comprehensive puncture repair kit, that includes new valve cores.

N.B. There are many makes of inner tube available, some of inferior manufacture. Make sure you purchase only those of a well known brand.

NEVER fit the wrong sized tube into a tyre; it is exceedingly dangerous to do so.

South African manufactured Goodyear G22, an absolute wolf in sheep's clothing. This is a superb tyre on road and extremely competent in sands. Very long lasting - this example was 5 years old with 60,000 miles use on a Defender 110. A 10 ply casing, with "running" tread pattern and small but sufficient side lugs; quiet and economical on road, tough enough to handle sharp rocks and gravel. However, not good in serious mud.

Avon Rangemaster, still a standard fit for UK built Defenders and a seriously undervalued tyre. Long lasting, tough, good in sand especially run soft, and with good mud grip. Almost unobtainable in Africa, but mixes well with other tread patterns.

REMEMBER - If you can't predict operating conditions, choose a tough, all purpose tyre.

4. TYRE LIFE AND ECONOMY - ON-ROAD:

Radial ply tyres in general last longer than cross-ply and have lower rolling resistance, which can improve fuel economy.

5. TYRES - OFF-ROAD:

Large diameter tyres offer better flotation, traction and under-axle clearance. Land Rover Ninety Models can be fitted with optional 7.50 x 16 tyres. One-Ten Land Rovers are so equipped as standard.

WARNING - Never mix radial and cross-ply tyres on one vehicle. Safe handllng may be seriously affected.

6. WHAT TO LOOK FOR:

Dual purpose on/off road use:

Where most driving will be on roads or good tracks and there is only a limited off-road requirement, dual purpose tyres offer good road life and performance and reasonable off-road traction. These tyres are unlikely to have an open 'knobbly' tread pattern.

Mud:

The knobbly tread tyre is designed to self-clean by throwing off mud to ensure continued grip. The penalty can be high on-road noise and only fair wet-road adhesion. Tyre chains on a 'road' tyre offer a time-consuming, messy but effective alternative. Tractor-type cleated tyres (special order only) are only suitable for general speeds of around 40 kph (25 mph), and so are only useful under exceptionally wet off-road conditions.

Snow:

For virgin snow, select a tyre which features the performance of a mud tyre. However most snow driving will be over compacted snow for which a less knobbly tyre works best. Consider chains for an effective and temporary solution.

Sand:

Hot, dry and sandy terrains demands a tyre with high flotation and good high temperature performance. It should also be capable of running on (temporarily) reduced pressures over soft sand. It should also be tough enough to withstand the sharp stones and thorns of semi-desert regions.

Toughness:

Don't mistake a knobbly tread pattern for toughness. For rocky ground, a tough thick tread is essential for good tyre life - the more reinforcing plies and tread rubber it has the better.

REMEMBER. The real strength of radial ply tyres is in the tread rather than the side walls. Drive over sharp stones rather than round them to avoid sidewall damage.

7. TYRE PRESSURES:

It is vital that tyres are kept at correct pressures for road speed otherwise damage through overheating will occur.

The recommended emergency low pressures for operating in difficult, soft off-road conditions can work very effectively - but under no circumstances should the vehicle be driven at over 40 kph (25 mph). Reinflate to correct pressures as soon as practicable. (See Section 5.L details of electric tyre inflators)

REMEMBER - Always maintain recommended tyre pressures and use 'soft' pressures sparingly to avoid tyre damage. Never exceed 40 kph (25 mph) on emergency soft inflation tyres.

Recommended tyre pressures - lb. sq. in (bar or kg. sq. cm)

		FRONT	REAR
90 MODELS	6.00 x 16 CROSSPLY	35 (2.4)	47 (3.3)
	7.50 X 16 CROSSPLY		
	& 205 R16 RADIAL PLY	28 (2.0)	35 (2.4)
	7.50 R16 RADIAL PLY	35 (2.4)	35 (2.4)
110 MODELS	7.50 X 16 CROSSPLY	28 (2.0)	42 (3.0)
	7.50 R16 RADIAL PLY	35 (2.4)	35 (2.4)

Emergency soft tyre pressures

UNLADEN	90 & 110 MODELS	16 (1.1) FRONT
AND REAR		
LADEN 90 MODELS	16 (1.1) FRONT	23 (1.6) REAR

1.I LAND ROVER WORLDWIDE DISTRIBUTORS - VEHICLES, PÅRTS AND SERVICE.

At the time of going to press Land Rover's distribution in both the UK and worldwide is in a state of flux because of Ford's take-over of the company from BMW.

For information concerning the current status of a dealer/distributor with regard to vehicle availability and servicing facilities we would recommend in the UK that readers contact Land Rover Customer Service Centre at:

Land Rover UK, Warwick Technology Park, Warwick, Warwickshire, CV34 6RG. Tel. 44 (0) 8705 000 500

or refer to the website: www.landrover.com.

For information covering Southern Africa - Land Rover South Africa has an excellent website: www.landrover.co.za and are based at:

Simon Vermooten Road, Silverton PO Box 411, Pretoria, 0001 South Africa. Tel: 27 (0)12 842-3227 Fax: 27 (0)12 842-3331

email: crc@landrover.co.za

1.J LAND ROVER EXPORTS

To satisfy the demands of customers who require personal service and advice for the exportation of vehicles from the UK, Land Rover have established an office in London to handle personal export sales and parts etc. They are:

Land Rover Export, 14 Berkeley Street, London. W1 8NF

Tel. 44 (0) 207 514 0405 Fax.. 44 (0) 207 629 9005

A further office has been set up in Dubai to handle export business for Africa and the Gulf states. They can be reached at:

Land Rover (Middle East & Africa), 16th Fioor, 1703 API World Tower, Sheikh Zayed Road, DUBAI, UAE PO Box 32588.

Tel: 97 (0)14 3327377   Fax: 97 (0)14 3313839

Both organisations will be pleased to provide information on vehicles, additional equipment and spares etc., for the current range of Land Rover models as well as advise on warranty support etc.

2. WHAT SPARES?

2. WHAT SPARES?

How to assess your parts needs - this section offers guidance on how to build up an adequate and relevant parts kit, how to work out what you will need for an extended period, where and from whom you should get them and how to store them so that they are in good condition when you need to use them.

CONTENTS

2.A INTRODUCTION

Spare parts are an essential part of the overall plan which will keep a Land Rover working hard for you.

Though Land Rover Defenders are designed and built to operate with a minimum of maintenance, if you intend doing it yourself, you will need to be equipped with the essentials.

This section shows you how to decide what you need, how to get them and how to look after them.

The only parts you should use are GENUINE Land Rover Parts which are available through Land Rover's sister company Land Rover Parts and its franchised outlets.

The reason is that parts available through unofficial channels are of highly variable quality and authenticity. Each part of a Land Rover goes to make up a vehicle of total design integrity. Spurious parts are weak links in every sense of the phrase.

For this reason, the fitting of any non-Genuine Parts may invalidate your warranty.

1. IN-TERRITORY DISTRIBUTOR:

The most convenient source of Genuine Parts will be the dealer closest to your destination. In most developing countries, there will at least be a distributor in the capital city. See Section 1.1 .

2. EXPORT DISTRIBUTOR:

A parts kit should be sent out with the Land Rover that is being exported. Talk to a your Export Distributor about this - an inexperienced supplier may fill your vehicle with parts you won't need and leave out parts you will want.

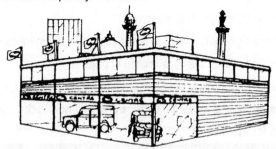

See Section 1.J for names and addresses of Export Distributors.

3. OTHER FRANCHISED AND NON-FRANCHISED DEALERS:

Avoid buying parts for EXPORT from dealers not approved as you may end up with unsuitable parts, incorrect advice and could even face importation problems on arrival at the vehicle's destination.

2.C PARTS KIT - HOW MANY?

Though it is difficult to predict which parts will need replacing and how often, it is possible to accurately assess your needs for service parts since there are fixed intervals for their replacement.

Any part that isn't a service part is categorised here as a precaution part - e.g., a replacement fan belt. The chart below is designed to give you an at-a-glance reference guide, taking into account the factors you may encounter.

Bear in mind that all aspects of the driving environment can influence and change the consumption of parts.

REMEMBER - choosing the correct Land Rover Defender, driving it carefully and loading it with care wlll all help reduce your demand for spares.

2.D PARTS KIT - WHICH ONES?

How do you work out what parts you will need for a Defender 110 Station Wagon which will operate in Western Sudan for two years?

Ask us. We will need to know the type of vehicle, the size of fleet, intended use, duration of use, experience of driver(s), where it will be used and the type of terrain over which it will operate.

We will put together a list for your individual requirements. General Parts lists are available from:

Land Rover International HQ, Gallows Hill,

Warwick Technology Park, Warwick, England CV34 3RG.

Tel: 44 1926 482396   Fax: 44 1926 483580

Email: lricc@landrover.com

REMEMBER - the more information you give us, the more accurate the parts list will be.

1. HOW MANY SPARES PER VEHICLE?

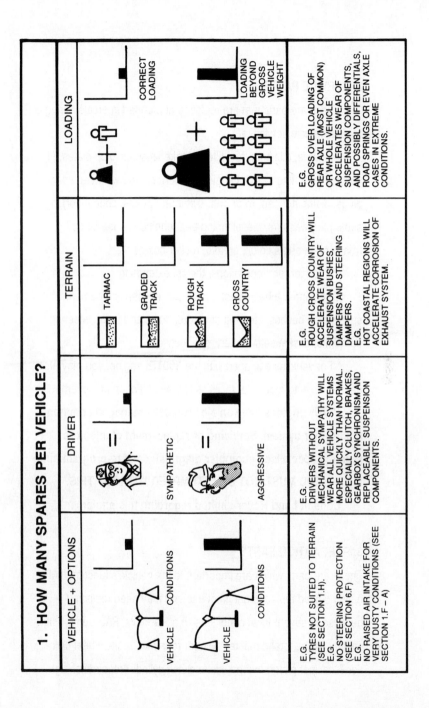

VEHICLE + OPTIONS	DRIVER	TERRAIN	LOADING
VEHICLE CONDITIONS VEHICLE CONDITIONS	SYMPATHETIC AGGRESSIVE	TARMAC GRADED TRACK ROUGH TRACK CROSS COUNTRY	CORRECT LOADING LOADING BEYOND GROSS VEHICLE WEIGHT
E.G. TYRES NOT SUITED TO TERRAIN (SEE SECTION 1.H). E.G. NO STEERING PROTECTION (SEE SECTION 6.F) E.G. NO RAISED AIR INTAKE FOR VERY DUSTY CONDITIONS (SEE SECTION 1.F – A)	E.G. DRIVERS WITHOUT MECHANICAL SYMPATHY WILL WEAR ALL VEHICLE SYSTEMS MORE QUICKLY THAN NORMAL. ESPECIALLY CLUTCH, BRAKES, GEARBOX SYNCHRONISM AND REPLACEABLE SUSPENSION COMPONENTS.	E.G. ROUGH CROSS COUNTRY WILL ACCELERATE WEAR OF SUSPENSION BUSHES, DAMPERS AND STEERING DAMPERS. E.G. HOT COASTAL REGIONS WILL ACCELERATE CORROSION OF EXHAUST SYSTEM.	E.G. GROSS OVER LOADING OF REAR AXLE (MOST COMMON) OR WHOLE VEHICLE ACCELERATES WEAR OF SUSPENSION COMPONENTS, AND POSSIBLY DIFFERENTIALS, ROAD SPRINGS OR EVEN AXLE CASES IN EXTREME CONDITIONS.

2. SERVICE PARTS

These are parts that are replaced at planned intervals during a regular vehicle service, e.g.

Air filters, oil filters, fuel filters, brake linings, clutch plates, (if you are operating a petrcl engined Defender, you will need spark plugs, distributor cap, rotor arm, distributor points, condensor), sump plug washers, diesel timing belt, engine oil, gearbox oil, transfer box and axle oil, grease, rocker box gaskets.

For longer term operations, the list extends to:

Tyres, inner tubes, injector nozzles*, suspension dampers, suspension bushes, steering dampers, bulbs and fuses, steering ball joints, gasket sets, battery, exhaust.

* For vehicles equipped with the **300TDI** engine, you may also need an injector pump, or facilities for re-calibration and overhaul.

** TD5 engines have an electronically managed common rail injector system. Servicing or replacement of injectors requires specialised computer diagnostic and re-programming facility, AND MUST NOT BE ATTEMPTED WITHOUT THIS.

Consult Land Rover Limited regarding this equipment.

3. PRECAUTION PARTS

These are parts which are important to the vehicle's function, but have no fixed replacement timetable and may need replacing because of severe local conditions. E.g., fanbelts, PAS pump belt, coolant hoses, brake master cylinder repair kit, brake wheel cylinder & calliper piston overhaul kits, clutch cylinder repair kits, high tension leads, ignition coil, road springs, track rods and steering gear. Facet fuel lift pump, universal joint replacement kits, wheel hub drive members, set rear axle half shafts, flexible turbo tube hoses.

Unless you are certain that these parts can be obtained quickly and easily enough not to seriously interfere with the vehicle's operation, a decision to invest in a supply of precaution parts should be regarded as a valuable 'insurance policy'.

4. TYPICAL PARTS PLAN FOR 110 DEFENDER

The following list is a typical SERVICE PARTS ONLY 'scaling plan' for a one-off vehicle which will be operated in a typically remote part of Africa for a year. This is included as an example only - consult Land Rover Parts Ltd or a UK based Export Distributor for your own requirements (see 2.D and 1.J for details). The part numbers shown were correct at the time of going to press but may be changed due to the continuing process of improving Land Rover products.

LAND ROVER TYPE: 110 SW   NO.VEHICLES: One

INTENDED USE: Relief/refugee   DURATION: One year

TYPE OF DRIVER: Local   TERRAIN: Hot, dusty - rough tracks, no metalled or sealed roads. Heavy duty use.

QUANTITY	PART NO	DESCRIPTION
	MANUALS	
1	RTC9863	Parts catalogue
1	LSM16WM	Workshop manual
	ENGINE ASSEMBLY	
15	AFU1881L	Joint Washer - sump plug
1	ERC7763	Belt timing - super torque
10	ETC6599	Element - oil filter

CLUTCH
TRANSMISSION:

4		Universal joint replacement kits
2		Wheel hub drive members
1	FRC0148	Clutch plate
1	FRC8573	Clutch cover
1	FRC9568	Release bearing assy

SUSPENSION

8	575582	Bush - radius arm
4	NRC4514	Bush - radius arm to chassis
6	NRC9278	Bush - Panhard Rod
4	NRC8455	Shock absorber - front
24	552818	Cushion rubber - shock absorber
4	NRC7491	Mounting rubber - Link to frame
4	RTC3455	Shock absorber - rear

STEERING

3	NTC1165	Steering damper

BRAKES - FRONT

3	RTC3348	Disc pad - axle set

BRAKES - REAR

6	RTC3418	Brake shoes - axle set
1	RTC3403	Brake shoe set - Transmission

FUEL SYSTEM

8	247179	Washer joint - injector
8	272474	Washer, sealing - injector

AIR CLEANER

6	NRC9238	Element

FUEL SYSTEM

14	90517711	Element - fuel filter

ENGINE ELECTRICS

1	RTC3215	Brush set - alternator

ELECTRICAL

1	RTC 3683	Light unit LHS - headlamp
4	264590	Bulb
4	264591	Bulb
4	570822	Bulb
3	RTC4482	Fuse 5 amp
3	RTC4500	Fuse 10 amp
3	RTC4502	Fuse 15 amp
3	RTC4505	Fuse 25 amp

GENERAL

2	MTC5084	Mirror head
6	7.50x16	Inner tube

OILS AND LUBRICANTS

2	x 5 Litres of ATF gearbox oil
14	x 5 Litres of engine oil
15	x 1litre of Hypoid 90
4	x 500ml Universal brake and clutch fluid

1. INDIVIDUAL PARTS

All parts for export use should be packed individually or in easily resealable packaging. The moment a parts multipack is opened for the first one to be removed, the remainder begin to deteriorate - dust, dirt and rust can quickly render them unuseable. A dust-filled replacement air filter will do more harm than good!

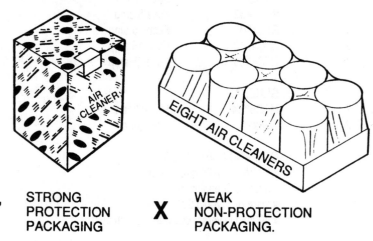

✔ STRONG PROTECTION PACKAGING

X WEAK NON-PROTECTION PACKAGING.

Individual parts packaging must permit identity checks without opening. Land Rover Genuine Parts packaging are both resealable and easily checked.

2. CRATING FOR EXPORT

Assume the very worst treatment for your parts packaging as it travels to its destination - and pack accordingly.

Weatherproof stout wooden crates, generously filled with shock absorbing material tightly packed around the spares, are ideal.

Clearly mark each box's contents, weight and destination. 'Fragile' and 'This Way Up' markings can be helpful but not everyone can read. Use the international symbols.

3. PARTS CRATING FOR REMOTE AREAS

Individual parts correctly crated for export to developing countries always appear to be over-packed by European standards. A box of spares is likely to be manhandled roughly and/or left open to the elements. For these reasons we recommend that you tightly pack all parts in wooden, sealed crates clearly marked as to contents, weight and destination. As people handling crates cannot see inside them it is worth marking them with "this way up" and "fragile" if applicable - there are international symbols for showing this. See below for suggested maximum dimensions and weights for transporting spares to remote areas.

A common irritation is for a long awaited box of spares to arrive, only to find that a majority of parts are unserviceable due to weak, loose packing coupled with rough handling - very frustrating.

MAXIMUM CRATE WEIGHT = 200 KG
MAXIMUM SIZE 1.5M x 1.5M x 1.5M (SMALLER BETTER)
STOUT WOODEN CRATES THE BEST!

MAN HANDLING:–
MAX SAFE LIFTING
PER MAN = 25 KG

2.F PARTS ORDERING FROM REMOTE AREAS - HOW?

Parts ordering can be a low priority when there are other more pressing tasks to be carried out. It is often left to the last minute as a scrawled addition to weekly or monthly despatches.

If the message isn't clearly understood because of hasty writing or a misread part number, the result can be weeks and even months of delay.

For your own sake, use the sample order form as a model for your orders. Always give all the details indicated.

LAND ROVER SPARES ORDER   REF: 00458

CATALOGUE: ONE-TEN   RTC 9863 cc   FEB 87
VEHICLE CHASSIS NOS: SALLDHMCBBA 299700

NO. OFF	PART NUMBER	DESCRIPTION	PAGE REF	COST OFFICE USE ONLY.
2	NRC 8455	SHOCK ABSORBER - FRONT	E 30	
10	9051771	ELEMENT - FUEL FILTER	H 36	

REMEMBER - Stick to the description in the parts list - adding colourful 'extra' information may lead to misunderstandings.

2.G PARTS STORAGE - WHERE AND HOW TO DO IT

Once you have received the parts you ordered, don't forget to look after them. Keep them under cover from sun and rain, securely locked (motor parts are a universal currency) and ensure that the parts store is as free from dust and dirt as your kitchen.

For a small fleet of vehicles, a wooden box may be adequate (but beware of termites)

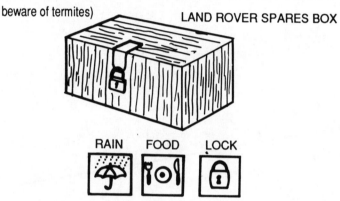

LAND ROVER SPARES BOX

RAIN   FOOD   LOCK

Simple shelving can become a tidy, organised and easily managed parts store. Be sure to fix the shelves securely and test for strength by standing on the shelves, starting at the lowest one.

TYPICAL SHELVING SUITABLE FOR LAND ROVER SPARES

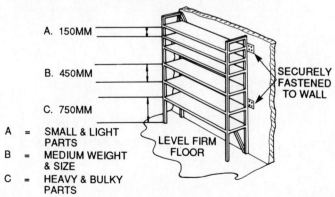

A. 150MM

B. 450MM

C. 750MM

SECURELY
FASTENED
TO WALL

LEVEL FIRM
FLOOR

A = SMALL & LIGHT PARTS
B = MEDIUM WEIGHT & SIZE
C = HEAVY & BULKY PARTS

REMEMBER - Always keep a written record of your parts stock and consumption - it will help you plan ahead.

REMEMBER - Depending on the extent of your parts store, organising your parts shelves in catalogue order - e.g. Shock absorbers under Section E - will make them easier to locate.

3. WHO DRIVES?

3. WHO DRIVES?

Selecting, assessing and training drivers to drive a Land Rover efficiently, safely and economically – this section includes an eye-test technique, a pictorial guide to off-road driving techniques and practical advice on correctly loading a vehicle. It also includes an extensive table of improvised repairs for emergencies.

CONTENTS
PART ONE

PART TWO - IN DEPTH

3.A INTRODUCTION

The more accomplished that people are at driving a Land Rover, the less stressful they find off-road driving - and the less time the vehicle spends in the workshop.

Better drivers make better use of the Land Rover and training people to be better drivers is a short-term investment with long term benefits.

3.B DRIVER TRAINING

People who are to drive Land Rovers in a developing country should be taught how to do the job properly before they depart. All the basic off-road techniques which will form the basis of their skills can be taught in three ways:

1. Land Rover Experience$^{©}$ training courses

2. By a visiting instructor at a customer-specified location.

3. Select any one of a number of specialised driving schools which offer instruction in off-road techniques (see specialist magazine adverts).

A driving techniques booklet and instruction course on video tape is available from Land Rover - see Section 7.M General items for details.

Driving in remote areas calls for more than simple driving skills. Vehicle operators should also be trained to cope with simple preventive maintenance, improvised repairs and basic first aid needs.

3.C DRIVER TRAINING - IN-TERRITORY

Though it is a serious business, the assessment and training of existing and potential drivers can be effectively carried out with the organisation of a 'skills' day.

By pitting drivers against each other in an untimed auto-test style event which calls for controlled precision driving - manoeuvering through tight turns and between narrow gaps on a course marked by bamboo canes - the fleet manager can see what needs to be done to improve standards.

An event like this can double as a valuable morale raiser as well as being a subtle and diplomatic way of improving driving standards.

REMEMBER - all new drivers should be given a probationary trial during which bad habits can be noted and corrected. If not, the penalty can emerge later in workshop costs.

Try to find time to devise a test route on which you can observe your drivers' skills - experience has shown that it is worthwhile combining all possible techniques, local terrains and hazards into one route, say, 10 kilometres long.

SKILLS TESTED SHOULD INCLUDE (AS APPROPRIATE):

1. Changing gear smoothly - especially between high and low ranges.
2. Climbing, descending and traversing hills.
3. Obstacle crossing - ridges and ditches.
4. Low traction - mud and soft sand.
5. Wading - if applicable.
6. General driving skills.

DRIVING TEST LOOK OUT FOR:

1. Is he/she sympathetic to the mechanics of the vehicle? e.g. no crash during gear changes, avoidance of potholes/bumps, gentle use of controls.

2. Does he/she position the vehicle well? - e.g. at road junctions, away from the crown of the road, and when selecting an off-road route.

3. Does he/she drive with consideration to other road users? - e.g. clear indication of direction changes, safe overtaking, care for pedestrians and animals.

4. Does he/she drive at a suitable speed under all conditions? - e.g. obey speed limits if in force, not drive too fast for rough ground, no skidding round bends.

5. Does he/she appear observant? - e.g. use of rear mirror, anticipation of potential hazards, slowing down for children, etc. For a visual guide to off-road driving techniques designed for use as a teaching aid, see Section 3.I Driving Off-Road.

SIGHT TESTS

The most obvious but often overlooked requirement of a driver is clear vision. Check your driver's eyes with the Sheridan Gardner-based symbol test shown overleaf.

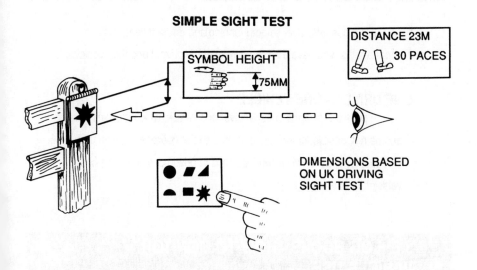

SIMPLE SIGHT TEST

SYMBOL HEIGHT 75MM

DISTANCE 23M 30 PACES

DIMENSIONS BASED ON UK DRIVING SIGHT TEST

This test simply requires a person to look at a symbol from a set distance and then indicate which one it is from a selection on a hand-held card.

3.D DRIVER/VEHICLE POLICY - WHO DRIVES WHICH VEHICLE?

For a cost-effective, smooth running and efficient fleet, it is important that you have effective control of the drivers and their vehicles.

ONE DRIVER - ONE VEHICLE

If possible, allocate to each driver one vehicle which they will drive and be responsible for looking after. You can encourage this with the introduction of a monthly incentive bonus or prize scheme for the best vehicle/driver team.

3.E LOG BOOKS - HOW TO MONITOR VEHICLE USE

If your drivers can read and write, introduce personal vehicle log books. Though drivers are always reluctant to get involved in paperwork, log books will help you identify future fuel, oil, service and spare part requirements and help you run your fleet efficiently.

Each log book should record trip distance, fuel, oil and water fill-ups and feature a problems section. It should also be used to log all servicing details, next service, minor and major rectification.

It can also provide drivers with a straightfoward checklist to carry out before starting a journey or a day's work.

For details of the simple vehicle log card system and a checklist from which one tailored for your drivers can be drawn up, see Section 5.M Vehicle Admin.

3.F ROUTINE CHECKS - HOW CAN DRIVERS HELP?

Routine checks highlight hidden or potential problems and encourage preventive maintenance. Divided into daily and weekly checks, these are carried out in addition to scheduled servicing.

Daily checks are carried out by the driver alone. Weekly checks are carried out with the assistance of a mechanic and can include spot checks by the vehicle or workshop supervisor.

DAILY CHECKS - should be carried out by the driver at the beginning of each working day.

1. DAILY VEHICLE CHECKS

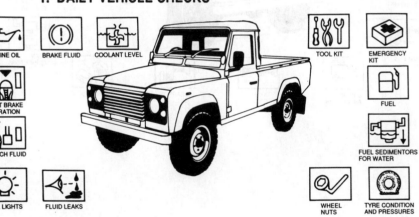

ENGINE OIL   BRAKE FLUID   COOLANT LEVEL   TOOL KIT   EMERGENCY KIT

FOOT BRAKE OPERATION   FUEL

CLUTCH FLUID   FUEL SEDIMENTORS FOR WATER

ALL LIGHTS   FLUID LEAKS   WHEEL NUTS   TYRE CONDITION AND PRESSURES

WEEKLY CHECKS – In addition to daily checks – should be carried out by the mechanic and the driver.

2. ADDITIONAL WEEKLY VEHICLE CHECKS

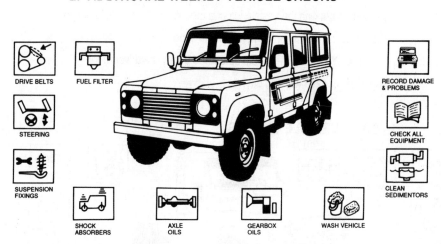

DRIVE BELTS

FUEL FILTER

RECORD DAMAGE & PROBLEMS

STEERING

CHECK ALL EQUIPMENT

SUSPENSION FIXINGS

CLEAN SEDIMENTORS

SHOCK ABSORBERS

AXLE OILS

GEARBOX OILS

WASH VEHICLE

3.G LOADING - HOW MUCH CAN A LAND ROVER DEFENDER CARRY?

Loading must be carried out with care if the vehicle's stability and driveability is not to be affected.

The load should be evenly distributed, with weight concentrated forward of the rear axle.

A carefully loaded Land Rover Defender loses little of the empty vehicle's ability to tackle side slopes and rough or undulating terrain.

REMEMBER - a correctly fully-loaded Land Rover Defender (Gross Vehicle Weight) should have about 50mm (2" between the front bump rubber and axle pad - the rubber at the rear should have 75mm (3") clearance between the bump rubber and axle pad.

Do not exceed payload maximum weight (see vehicle handbook and overleaf for data).

(EEC Payload is the maximum recommended cargo weight of the vehicle in addition to a driver and a full tank of fuel).

1. EXAMPLES OF LOADING A LAND ROVER DEFENDER 110

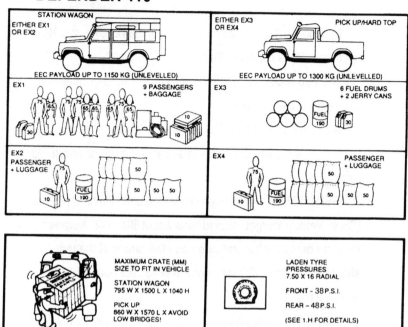

If a roof rack is required, fit only an approved product and remember that the maximum load for the rack is **150 Kg including the weight of the rack itself.**

Use the roof rack only when there is no space left inside the vehicle - and arrange the load so that heavy material goes inside and light kit on top.

2. EFFECT OF LOAD ON VEHICLE STABILITY

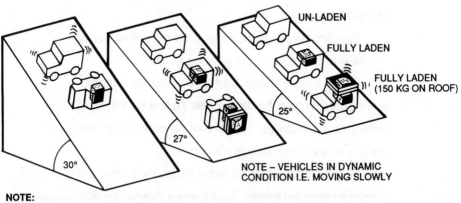

UN-LADEN

FULLY LADEN

FULLY LADEN
(150 KG ON ROOF)

25°

27°

30°

NOTE – VEHICLES IN DYNAMIC
CONDITION I.E. MOVING SLOWLY

**NOTE:
TERRAIN MAY
REDUCE ANGLES SHOWN**

REMEMBER - roof racks enable you to carry more volume, not extra weight. Ignoring the limit can lead to damage to the vehicle and accidents.

3.H THE ENVIRONMENT - HOW YOU CAN HELP PRESERVE IT

All drivers should be aware of the serious damage that can be inflicted on the fragile ecology of a semi-desert area through thoughtlessness.

Deep tyre ruts cut into the top soil by spinning wheels can alter natural water courses leading to increased soil erosion.

Strike a balance between creating new ruts and making the existing ones too deep. Avoid driving over the flora that may be all that is holding the topsoil together. Steer clear of the young saplings which should one day provide badly needed shade.

Remember that even in the wilderness you share tracks and by-ways with people and animals. Spare them the choking dust cloud thrown up by a speeding vehicle and people will be more likely to offer help when you need it.

If you have the time, help keep tracks in reasonable repair by filling deep potholes. Moving fallen trees which are blocking tracks will avoid the need to start new tracks through fresh ground.

Hot brakes and exhausts can start fires when a vehicle is stopped close to or in dry grass land.

The fuel and lubricants in your vehicle are mildly toxic. Dispose of them carefully to avoid pollution, especially of drinking water sources. They can be useful - old engine oil painted onto timber or sacking can act as an insect repellant and diesel oil is a smelly but effective disinfectant for concrete floors.

3.I DRIVING OFF-ROAD - A PICTORIAL GUIDE

AT THE WHEEL

GROUND RULES

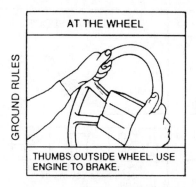

THUMBS OUTSIDE WHEEL. USE ENGINE TO BRAKE.

OBSTACLE CROSSING

GROUND RULES

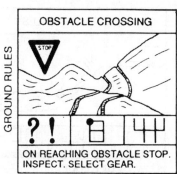

ON REACHING OBSTACLE STOP. INSPECT. SELECT GEAR.

USE THE GEARS

GROUND RULES

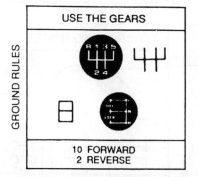

10 FORWARD
2 REVERSE

SOFT GROUND

ON THE LEVEL

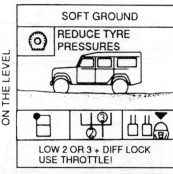

REDUCE TYRE PRESSURES

LOW 2 OR 3 + DIFF LOCK
USE THROTTLE!

ROUGH TRACKS

ON THE LEVEL

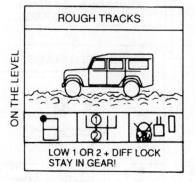

LOW 1 OR 2 + DIFF LOCK
STAY IN GEAR!

DITCH CROSSING

ON THE LEVEL

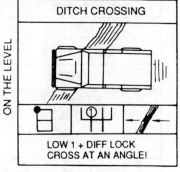

LOW 1 + DIFF LOCK
CROSS AT AN ANGLE!

DESCENDING HILLS

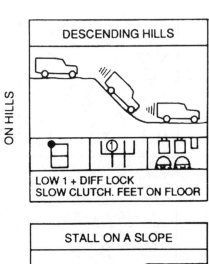

LOW 1 + DIFF LOCK
SLOW CLUTCH. FEET ON FLOOR

STALL ON A SLOPE

APPLY BRAKE. STALL ENGINE
HOLD BRAKE. LOW R + DIFF
LOCK

STALL ON A SLOPE

BRAKES OFF. TURN KEY.
FEET ON FLOOR

CROSSING RIDGES

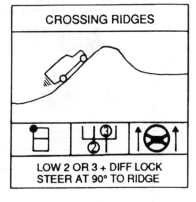

LOW 2 OR 3 + DIFF LOCK
STEER AT 90° TO RIDGE

SIDE SLOPES

LOW 2 OR 3 + DIFF LOCK
STEER STRAIGHT AHEAD

'V' SHAPED GULLEY

LOW 2 OR 3 + DIFF LOCK
STEER STRAIGHT AHEAD

THROUGH WATER

WADING

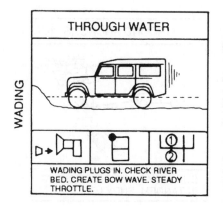

WADING PLUGS IN. CHECK RIVER BED. CREATE BOW WAVE. STEADY THROTTLE.

WHEN CLEAR

WADING

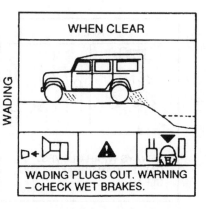

WADING PLUGS OUT. WARNING – CHECK WET BRAKES.

DEEP WATER

WADING

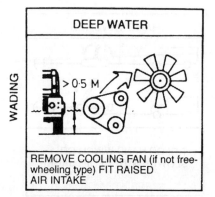

> 0·5 M

REMOVE COOLING FAN (if not free-wheeling type) FIT RAISED AIR INTAKE

TOWING POINTS

TOWING

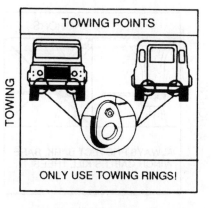

ONLY USE TOWING RINGS!

TOWING

TOWING

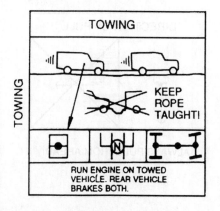

KEEP ROPE TAUGHT!

RUN ENGINE ON TOWED VEHICLE. REAR VEHICLE BRAKES BOTH.

SUSPENDED TOW

TOWING

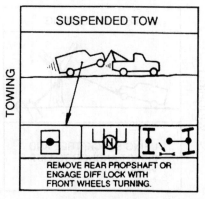

REMOVE REAR PROPSHAFT OR ENGAGE DIFF LOCK WITH FRONT WHEELS TURNING.

WINCHING

SAFETY

ALWAYS WEAR GLOVES. CABLES CAN BREAK. STAND CLEAR.

GROUND ANCHORS ⚓
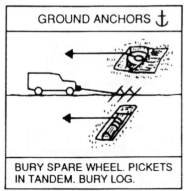
BURY SPARE WHEEL. PICKETS IN TANDEM. BURY LOG.

TREES AS ANCHORS
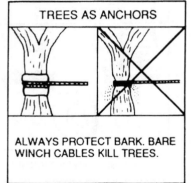
ALWAYS PROTECT BARK. BARE WINCH CABLES KILL TREES.

HAND WINCHES
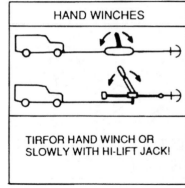
TIRFOR HAND WINCH OR SLOWLY WITH HI-LIFT JACK!

VEHICLE LIFTING
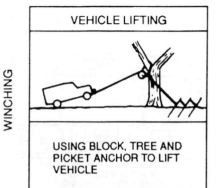
USING BLOCK, TREE AND PICKET ANCHOR TO LIFT VEHICLE

DIRECTION OF PULL
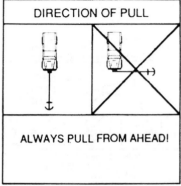
ALWAYS PULL FROM AHEAD!

TWENTY-FIVE STEPS TO SAFE WINCHING

Anyone can become proficient at winching. It is not necessarily an art, but it does require a thorough awareness on the part of the user, as to the capabilities of his winch and equipment coupled with sound knowledge of how to get the best from them.

Listed here is a guide of do's and don'ts of winching operations. Some will be obvious, some not so. All, though, will lead to safer winching.

(1) BEFORE winching with an electric winch, inspect the remote control lead for cracks, pinched wiring, fraying or loose connections. A damaged, shorted lead could cause the winch to operate as soon as it is plugged in.

(2) Only plug in the remote control lead when you want to use the winch.

(3) When the remote control lead is plugged in **ALWAYS** keep it clear of the drum fairlead area, the rope and any rigging.

(4) **ALWAYS** store the control lead in a clean dry area where it cannot be damaged.

(5) When using the remote control from inside the vehicle, **ALWAYS** pass the lead through the window to avoid trapping the lead in the door.

(6) **ALWAYS** stand well clear of wire rope and load during winching operations. Insist that helpers/spectators keep to a safe distance when winching.

(7) **ALWAYS** use vehicle ground anchors when recovering another vehicle.

(8) **ALWAYS** be sure that an anchor point intended for use is strong enough to withstand the load applied.

(9) **ALWAYS** use a choker chain, wire rope made for the purpose or tree trunk protector when connecting the winch wire to an anchor point.

(10) **ALWAYS** use a tree trunk protector when a tree is used as an anchor point.

(11) **ALWAYS** check that when ground or vehicle anchors are used the anchor is firm throughout the duration of the pull.

(12) **ALWAYS** keep a check on the winch wire anchor point; under heavy load it could fail with disastrous consequences.

(13) **ALWAYS** inspect and carefully re-wind wire rope after use. Crushed, pinched or frayed areas severely reduce original tensile strength. (For safety's sake, wire rope should be replaced when any form of damage is evident).

(14) **ALWAYS** stop winching when the hook is at least 3 metres away from the fairlead of the winch.

Always attach your winch rope to a tree protector. A chain around a tree will certainly hold but may ring-bark the tree. A length of timber inserted on the opposite side to the pull will minimise damage to the bark.

(15) **ALWAYS** wear gloves. Do not let wire rope slide through bare hands.

(16) **ALWAYS** use proper vehicle anchor points. Never hook up to bumpers, spring hangers or axle casings. When recovering an old vehicle be aware of the condition of the vehicle's anchor points.

(17) Ensure that the rope is correctly spooled onto the winch drum. The spooling (winding-on) of the wire rope can be accidentally reversed by running the rope all the way out and re-spooling in with remote control switch in the 'power-out' mode.

(18) **NEVER** handle wire rope or rigging during winching operations or touch a wire rope or its hook while they are under tension; even when the winch is not in operation there may still be a considerable load applied to winch and cable.

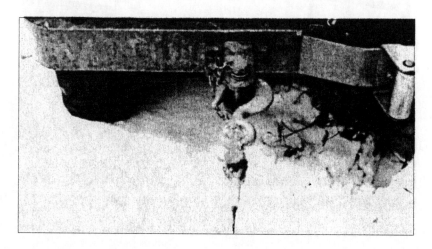

Only hook cables to anchor points that are specifically designed for the purpose.

(19) **NEVER** put a wire winch rope round an anchor and hook it back on itself, as this will damage the wire rope and reduce its tensile strength.

(20) **NEVER** operate a winch with less than 5 wraps of wire rope on the drum. A winch drum with fewer than 5 wraps of the rope remaining may break loose under load conditions.

(21) **NEVER** exceed the capacity of the winch. Use a pulley block to double the line-pull which will almost halve the load on the winch and the wire rope.

A minium of 5 coils of wire should always be left on the drum. It would be useful to paint a yellow mark on the cable as the final sixth coil on the drum appears at the fairlead.

(22) **NEVER** use the winch to tow another vehicle. The braking system on winches is not designed for this sort of abuse and the sudden jerking will eventually cause the wire rope to snap.

(23) **NEVER** stand astride or step over the cable when winching.

(24) **IMPORTANT:** When re-spooling cable, **ALWAYS** release the control switch when the hook is a minimum of 1 metre from the fairlead and inch in the remaining cable onto the drum. This procedure is vital to personal safety and to avoid rope damage caused by over-tightening.

When winching and driving, keep tension on the winch wire. A sudden snatch, as the winch wire alternately becomes slack and takes the load again, will damage the winch and its cable, and will lead to premature cable failure.

(25) When starting winching, use the control switch intermittently to inch in any slack in the wire rope prior to taking the strain. This will reduce the chance of damage to the winch or wire rope from shock loadings (which could briefly exceed the winch's capacity)

Note the use of hand signals: Inching in the winch wire prior to taking the strain.

For further information on winching refer to Land Rover Publication SMR 699MI - WINCHING IN SAFETY.

LAND ROVER RECOMMENDED DRIVING PROCEDURES

PROCEDURES

The following notes are intended as a guide to Land Rover drivers in order that they may obtain maximum benefit from their vehicles when driving on or off road. This publication describes the basic techniques which apply to vehicles with manual transmission.

PERMANENT FOUR WHEEL DRIVE
Land Rover One Ten & Ninety 5 speed Defenders

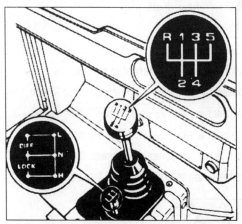

The Land Rover Defenders feature permanent four wheel drive as standard equipment with a lockable centre differential. The differential is locked by moving the transfer lever to the left of the gate in high or low range without depressing the clutch pedal. A fascia mounted warning light indicates when the differential is locked. Low range is engaged by bringing the vehicle to a standstill and pushing the transfer lever forward through the neutral position into low range.

Re-selecting high range would normally be done with the vehicle stationary, but if it is necessary to make the change on the move, the correct procedure should be followed as detailed in the section for towing.

Range Rover 4 speed and all V8 Land Rover Defenders have permanent four wheel drive transmission using lockable centre differential to prevent transmission wind up. This differential is locked by operating a tunnel mounted switch on the Range Rover and a similar switch on the V8 Land Rover which is mounted on the seat box below the centre seat position. The differential lock can be operated at any speed and it is not necessary to depress the clutch. A fascia mounted warning light indicates when the differential is locked.

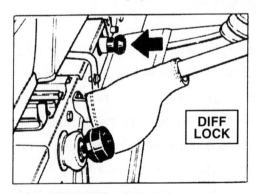

Low range is engaged by bringing the vehicle to a stop and pushing the transfer lever forward on the Range Rover, and down on the V8 Land Rover Defenders.

CORRECT GEAR SELECTION - LAND ROVER DEFENDERS

Differential Lock and Four Wheel Drive

The centre differential lock on permanent four wheel drive vehicles and the four wheel drive control on all other models should be engaged whenever rough, slippery, loose or uneven terrain is encountered. Both of these controls can be operated while the vehicle is moving but not if individual wheels are already spinning due to loss of traction, and in these circumstances the vehicle should be brought to a stop. Neither four wheel drive or the centre differential lock should be engaged on hard roads except under very slippery conditions as the differential speeds of rotation of the road wheels when cornering can cause transmission damage.

If the vehicle is fitted with free-wheel front hubs, they must be locked prior to engaging four wheel drive.

Low Range

Low range should only be selected for extreme off road conditions where progress in high range could not be maintained, or in any situation where low speed manoeuvring is necessary i.e. reversing a trailer or negotiating a boulder strewn river bed. In addition, when towing a heavy load it is often easier to move off in low range and then change into high range when a reasonable road speed has been achieved. Before driving through difficult ground conditions, select low range, remembering to engage the diff lock on permanent four wheel drive vehicles, and a suitable gear; in most conditions second or third gears on vehicles fitted with manual transmission, or 'D' on vehicles fitted with automatic transmission. Only experience will tell the driver which is the correct gear for a given section of ground, but generally with manual transmission, the higher the gear, the better. Do not change gear while negotiating difficult terrain as the drag at the wheels may cause the vehicle to stop when the clutch is depressed and difficulty may be experienced in restarting.

Exercise care when using the accelerator as sudden power surges may induce wheel spin.

As the ground conditions become less difficult, high range should be reselected remembering to remain in four wheel drive or to keep the differential lock engaged where there is any risk of losing traction.

SURVEY ON FOOT BEFORE DRIVING

Before negotiating a difficult section of terrain, it is a wise precaution to carry out a preliminary survey of the ground on foot in order to minimise the risk of getting caught in a previously unnoticed hazard.

Before driving through a difficult section, select low range and a suitable gear. For most purposes second or third gears will prove practical. Only experience will tell the driver which is the correct gear for a given section but generally the higher the gear, the better.

RIDING THE CLUTCH

This will result in premature clutch wear and could result in the driver losing control of the vehicle by inadvertantly depressing the clutch as the vehicle travels over a sudden bump.

SELECTABLE FOUR WHEEL DRIVE (all Series Land Rovers)

Series I, II and III Land Rover

Selectable four wheel drive is fitted as basic equipment to all Series Land Rovers. These vehicles are driven in two wheel drive high range under normal conditions, and four wheel drive and/or low range can be engaged when the ground conditions become difficult.

4 Wheel Drive – High Range :-

Four wheel drive high range is engaged by pushing down the lever with the yellow knob and this can be done without stopping the vehicle or depressing the clutch. Two wheel drive is regained by stopping the vehicle and pulling back the lever with the red knob (transfer lever) until the lever with the yellow knob returns to the two wheel drive position, then returning the transfer lever to its original position.

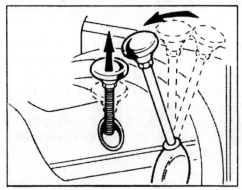

4 Wheel Drive – Low Range:-

Low range is engaged by bringing the vehicle to a complete standstill and then pulling the transfer lever back through the neutral position into low range. This also engages four wheel drive. High range is regained by returning the transfer lever to the fully forward position. This change is usually carried out with the vehicle stationary although it can be made on the move and this technique is fully described in the section covering towing.

BRAKING

Keep the application of the brake pedal to an absolute minimum. Braking on wet, muddy or loose surface slopes will almost certainly cause one or more wheels to lock and the resulting slide could prove dangerous.

ENGINE BRAKING

Before descending steep slopes, stop the vehicle and engage first gear low range on vehicles fitted with manual transmission or first gear hold in low range on automatic vehicles. While descending the slope it should be remembered that the engine will provide sufficient braking effort to control the speed of descent, and that the brakes should not be applied as this may cause the trailing wheels to lock on loose or slippery surfaces resulting in loss of control.

DRIVING ON SOFT GROUND

When driving through soft ground conditions, reduced tyre pressures will increase the contact area of the tyres with the ground. This will improve traction by increasing tyre flotation. It should be born in mind that reduced tyre pressures also reduce ground clearance and this could cause problems on deeply rutted tracks. The tyre pressures must be returned to normal as soon as possible. Refer to the vehicle instruction manual for advice on maximum and minimum tyre pressures.

DRIVING ON ROUGH TRACKS

Although rough tracks can be negotiated in two wheel drive, it is advisable to select four wheel drive if there is excessive suspension movement as this may induce wheel spin. On Range Rovers and Land Rovers fitted with permanent four wheel drive the centre differential should be locked.

As the track becomes rougher it may be necessary to engage low range to enable a steady low speed to be maintained without constant use of the brake and clutch pedals.

CLIMBING STEEP SLOPES

When climbing or descending slopes it is important to follow the fall line, as travelling diagonally may result in the vehicle sliding broadside down the slope. When climbing steep slopes, particularly if the surface is loose or slippery, the higher the gear used, the better, because this enables the driver to take advantage of vehicle momentum. Too much speed when climbing a hill with a bumpy surface can result in one or more wheels lifting causing the vehicle to lose traction and stop. In this case a slower approach may be more successful. Often traction can be improved by easing off the accelerator just before loss of forward motion.

1) If the vehicle fails to climb a hill but does not stall, the following procedure, which applies to vehicles fitted with automatic or manual transmission, should be adopted:–

   a) Hold the vehicle on the foot brake. It will be necessary to use the handbrake only if the foot brake fails to hold due to wet brake linings.

   b) Engage reverse gear low range as quickly as possible.

   c) Release the brakes and clutch simultaneously.

   d) Allow the vehicle to reverse down the slope using engine over run braking to control the speed of descent.

   e) Do not apply the brake pedal during the descent. Even a light application may cause the front wheels to lock and this would render the steering ineffective.

One Ten & Ninety

2) If the engine stalls while climbing the hill, the following procedure is recommended on vehicles fitted with manual transmission.

a) Hold the vehicle on the foot brake/hand brake.

b) Engage reverse gear low range and remove feet from brake and clutch pedals.

c) Start the engine in gear and allow the vehicle to reverse down the hill using engine over run braking to check the speed. A laden vehicle on a steep hill will start without the aid of the starter motor as soon as the brakes are released, if there is sufficient traction.

When back on level ground or where traction can be regained a faster approach and the resulting extra momentum will probably enable the hill to be climbed.

d) If the engine should stall on a vehicle fitted with automatic transmission, the brakes should be applied and the engine must be restarted before reversing down the hill as there will be no braking effort from the gearbox unless the engine is running.

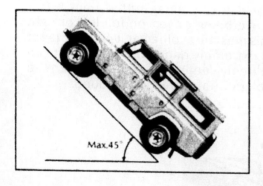

GROUND CLEARANCE

Remember the importance of maintaining ground clearance under the chassis and axle differentials and the necessity for clear approach and departure angles. Avoid deep wheel ruts, sudden changes in slope and obstacles which may foul the chassis or axles. On soft ground the axle differentials will clear their own patch in all but the most difficult conditions. However, on frozen, rocky or dry, hard ground, hard contact between the differentials and the ground will generally result in the vehicle coming to a sudden stop.

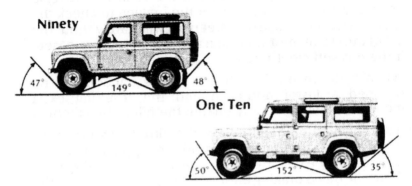

EXISTING WHEEL TRACKS

Avoid over-steering while driving along rutted tracks. This could result in the vehicle being driven on full left or right hand lock in the ruts. This must be avoided as it causes drag at the front wheels and is extremely dangerous because it can result in the vehicle suddenly veering off the track when the front wheels reach level ground or traction is found.

NEGOTIATING A
'V' SHAPED GULLY

This should be tackled with extreme caution, as steering up one or other of the gully walls could lead to the vehicle being trapped with its side against the gully wall.

CROSSING A RIDGE

Always approach a ridge at right angles so that both front wheels and then both rear wheels cross together. If approached at an angle traction can be lost completely through diagonally opposite wheels lifting off the ground.

CROSSING A DITCH

Ditches should always be crossed at an angle so that three wheels maintain contact with the ground assisting the passage of the fourth wheel through the ditch. If approached straight on, both front wheels will drop into the ditch probably with the chassis and the front bumper trapped on opposite sides of the ditch.

TRAVERSING A SLOPE

Traversing a slope should be undertaken having observed the following precautions:—

a) Check that the terrain is firm under all wheels and that the ground is not slippery.

b) Check that the downhill wheels are not likely to drop into a sudden depression in the ground as this will suddenly increase the angle of tilt.

c) For the same reason ensure that the uphill wheels do not run over rocks, tree roots, or similar obstacles.

d) Any load carried in the back of the vehicle should be evenly distributed as low as possible and made secure. A sudden shift of load while traversing a slope could cause the vehicle to overturn. Passengers in the rear should sit on the uphill side.

WADING

The maximum advisable fording depth is approximately 0.5 metres. Before negotiating a deep water crossing ensure that the clutch housing drain plug is in position, and if the water depth exceeds 0.5 metres removing the fan belt will eliminate the risk of the cooling fan spraying water over the ignition system and air cleaner. If, for various reasons, it is not possible to remove the fan belt, a sheet of plastic or other water resistant material draped in front of the radiator grille to prevent any water from passing through will reduce the risk of saturation of the ignition system.

Land Rover customers throughout the world frequently travel through water where the depth exceeds 0.5 m having taken the following precautions:–

a) Generally stagnant water is more likely to be a hazard than a river or stream as flowing water tends to prevent a build up of silt. The silt in a stagnant pool can be several feet deep. Always ensure that the river or pool bed is firm enough to support the weight of the vehicle and provide traction.

b) Ensure that the engine air intake is kept clear of the water.

c) A low gear is desirable and sufficient throttle should be maintained to avoid stalling the engine if the exhaust is under water.

d) Slow steady progress should be maintained to create a bow wave.

AFTER WADING

Make sure that the brakes are dried out as soon as possible so that they are effective when needed. This can be achieved by driving for a short distance with the brakes applied.

Refit the fan belt, remove the clutch housing drain plug and any covering material from the front of the radiator grille. If the water was particularly muddy it is possible that the radiator may be blocked with mud and leaves and this should be cleared immediately to reduce the risk of overheating.

If deep water is regularly negotiated it would be wise to check all transmission oils for signs of water contamination after each trip. Emulsified oil can be easily recognised by its milky appearance.

SOFT DRY SAND

It is generally advisable when driving in soft sand to use low range as this will enable you to accelerate through suddenly worsening conditions without the risk of being unable to restart, having stopped to change from high to low range.

Remember in soft conditions that reduced tyre pressures will increase the contact area with the ground but reference should first be made to the owners manual to ascertain the correct tyre pressures for the prevailing conditions. If the tyre pressures have been reduced for soft ground conditions they must be re-inflated upon regaining firm ground.

On vehicles fitted with manual transmission, gear changing should be kept to a minimum as depressing the clutch to change gear in soft sand will cause the vehicle to stop because of the drag at the wheels.

Vehicles fitted with three speed automatic transmission are best driven in these conditions in low range with the main selector lever in the second gear hold position, as this will eliminate unnecessary automatic gear changes which would make steady progress difficult to maintain.

When stopping your vehicle in sand remember that re-starting while facing up a slope is almost impossible and you should therefore park on level ground, or with the vehicle facing down hill. In order to avoid wheel spin a standing start is best achieved using second or third gear on manual transmission vehicles, and the minimum throttle opening that is necessary to start moving.

If forward motion is lost do not try to accelerate out of trouble as this can only make things worse. Clear the sand from the tyres and ensure that the chassis and axles are not touching the sand.

If the wheels have sunk deep into the sand it will be necessary to lift the vehicle using an air bag or high lift jack and then build up the sand under the wheels so that the vehicle, when lowered, will be on level ground. If a restart is still not possible it may be necessary to place sand mats or ladders beneath the wheels.

ICE AND SNOW

Land Rovers and Range Rovers are used extensively in snow and icy conditions and the driving techniques employed are generally similar to those used for driving on mud or wet grass. Select the highest gear possible in four wheel drive and drive away using the minimum throttle opening. Avoid violent movements of the steering wheel and keep braking to a minimum. The centre differential should be locked. Do not brake hard and drive slowly.

TOWING

When preparing the vehicle and trailer the following procedure should be adhered to:–

a) Adjust vehicle tyre pressures as recommended in the owners' manual.

b) Adjust trailer tyre pressures as recommended by the trailer manufacturer.

c) Balance the trailer and the vehicle, both unladen, so that with the trailer level, the drawbar is at the same height as the hitch point on the vehicle.

On vehicles fitted with 5 speed gearboxes and manual transmission, a smooth start will be achieved when towing trailers weighing more than 2000kg (4400 lb) by moving off in low range and then changing to high range on the move. The following procedure is recommended to avoid damage to the gearbox:–

a) Move off in first or second gear low range and increase the speed by changing through the gears to 25 - 30 km/h (15 - 20 mph).

b) Depress the clutch and move the transfer lever into neutral.

c) Remove your foot from the clutch pedal and allow the engine revs to drop to no more than 1000 rpm.

d) Depress the clutch pedal fully and immediately move the transfer lever into high range.

e) Select a gear suitable for the road speed obtained with the main gear lever.

The technique on vehicles fitted with V8 engines and 4 speed gearboxes is similar to above, the difference being that it is necessary to put the main lever into neutral before changing into high range.

DO NOT

a) The four wheel drive and differential lock controls should be engaged before driving onto any surface where traction may be lost at one or more wheels. Do not operate either of these controls while individual wheels are spinning.

b) Do not engage low range while the vehicle is moving.

c) Do not apply the handbrake while the vehicle is moving.

d) Do not allow the engine to labour in too high a gear.

e) Do not overload the vehicle for sustained cross country work. Reduce the payload by 90kg (198lbs).

f) Do not wrap your thumbs round the steering wheel as severe steering kick back over rough ground may result in a broken thumb.

g) Do not use the clutch pedal as a foot rest. Keep the left foot well clear of the clutch pedal while the vehicle is in motion.

h) Do not rely on the handbrake to hold the vehicle if the brake linings have been subjected to immersion in mud and water.

i) Do not engage the differential lock or four wheel drive on the road except when the road surface provides insufficient traction.

j) Do not continue to drive an automatic Range Rover if the transmission oil temperature warning light comes on. If this should happen, either position 2 or 1 should be engaged on the main gear selector lever, and if this fails to extinguish the light, low range should be engaged. If the warning light remains on in low range, the vehicle must be stopped and the engine left running with the main selector lever in neutral until the transmission oil cools down and the light is extinguished.

k) Do not allow the engine to idle for long periods with the main gear selector lever in the Park position.

GENERAL ADVICE ON VEHICLE RECOVERY

Should the vehicle become immobile due to loss of traction, the following hints will be of value:–

a) Once the vehicle is stationary, avoid prolonged wheel spin as this will only make matters worse.

b) Try to remove any obstacle i.e. rocks, tree stumps, etc. It will also help to remove any earth or sand that is supporting the weight of the vehicle via the chassis or axles.

c) If the ground is very soft, reduced tyre pressures may help. Remember that this will also reduce ground clearance.

e) Reverse as far as possible and the momentum gained by making a faster second approach may get the vehicle over the obstacle.

f) Brushwood, sacking or any similar material placed in front of the wheels will assist in obtaining traction.

g) If the vehicle has dug itself in, jack it up and build up the ground under the wheels to obtain ground clearance.

These are general guide lines and should help you to make use of the off road capabilities of Land Rovers. Careful thought and practical experience will usually provide the solution to any problems, but correct driving technique will itself ensure that such instances are kept to a minimum or avoided completely.

USEFUL DATA

	88"	109"	Ninety	One Ten
Approach Angle	46°	49°	47°	50°
Departure Angle	30°	24°	48°	35°
Max. Gradient	45°	45°	45°	45°
Min. Ground Clearance	178mm	209mm	198mm	215mm
Min. Turning Radius	5.8m	7.15m	5.75m	6.4m
Gross Vehicle Weight	2120kg	2710kg 3020kg H.C.P.U.	2400 standard 2550 high load	2950 levelled 3050 standard

TOWING CAPACITY

	On Road				Off Road
	88"	109"	Ninety	One Ten	All Models
Unbraked Trailers	500kg	500kg	500kg	500kg	500kg
Trailers with over-run brakes	2000kg	2000kg	3500kg	3500kg	1000kg
4 Wheel trailers with close coupled brakes	4000kg Petrol 3000kg Diesel	4000kg Petrol 3000kg Diesel	4000kg Petrol 3500kg Diesel 4000kg Turbo	4000kg	1000kg

3.J EMERGENCY ACTION - IMPROVISED REPAIRS FOR BREAKDOWNS

If your vehicle develops a problem when out in a remote area, there are a great number of steps you can take to diagnose and temporarily overcome the problem.

This section is designed to help you help yourself. The golden rule is: 'Don't Panic.' Sit down and think. Try to identify the problem. The diagnostic section in the Land Rover workshop manual can be very useful for this.

Some of the following ideas may provide sufficient temporary help in an emergency, although some may cause minor or even serious long-term damage and must be regarded as final resorts. The risks are identified in the text.

The techniques and ideas featured in this list have been collated from many sources other than the direct experience of Land Rover's own personnel. Not all have been proven by Land Rover official tests, so the information is given on trust.

The following improvised repairs for diesel engines **ARE NOT APPLICABLE TO THE TD5, AND MUST UNDER NO CIRCUMSTANCES BE ATTEMPTED FOR THESE ENGINES. The electronic management system for the TD5 incorporates a "get you home" back-up programme which automatically cuts in in the event of a main systems failure.**

PROBLEM	PROBABLE CAUSE	EMERGENCY CURE ONLY
Engine stops	No Fuel	Diesel engine can be run on kerosene or paraffin. Be sure to add 1 part engine oil to 100 parts kerosene ie 0.25L oil to 25L jerry can of fuel (The oil lubricates the pump)

> **The following applies ONLY to diesel engines up to 300TDI**

Split Fuel Line	Repair with PVC tape reinforced with wire. Monitor due to fire hazard. (Recommended for Diesel only)
Lift pump failure	Feed injection pump from jerry can mounted on roof rack. Don't let the jerry can drain completely to avoid need to re-prime system. Use accelerator lightly.
Blocked fuel line	Disconnect both ends and clear using footpump.
Fuel cut-off solenoid jammed shut	The shuttle in the solenoid can be removed but you will have to 'stall' vehicle to stop it.
Engine seized	It is likely that the engine will have seized on one cylinder only.
	Remove the piston (force will be needed), the conrod and the pushrods (to keep the valves

closed). Blank off the oil feed holes on the crankshaft journal with the bearing shells secured with a worm-drive clip or strong wire.

(For diesels, place a pipe over the injector pipe to divert fuel to a can)

Petrol engined vehicles	Ignition system fuse	If no replacement fuse, wrap fuse in metal foil or similar. Replace as soon as possible with correct fuse.
	Fuel pump defective	The screen wash pump can be used to pump fuel into the fuel line. When the engine starts to splutter, squirt more petrol in.

BEWARE - this method poses a serious fire risk and should only be used for dire emergencies only with fire fighting equipment available.

Broken contact breaker spring	The spring carries the current and holds the contact breaker against the distributor cam. Connect a wire across the join and press the heel against the cam with a piece of rubber.
	BEWARE - Short term use only.
Distributor cap carbon worn	Make a new brush out out of pencil lead, rolled up foil or the core from a dry cell torch battery.
Cracked distributor cap	Clean the crack thoroughly and fill with Araldite adhesive or melted rubber.
Faulty condensor	Smooth out a sheet of aluminium foil and cut a piece approximately 200mm long by 6mm. Stick this along the centre of a strip of plastic insulating tape, place a thin bolt at one end and roll the tape around it with the foil on the inside.

Alternatively, a pair of aluminium vehicle registration plates separated by insulating material ie plastic sheet, and lashed together with tape can be used. Ensure that only one plate is earthed to the vehicle.

No charge	Defective alternator	If you are operating in a convoy, your battery can be exchanged with one from another vehicle. Repeat exchange every 100 kms to prevent full drain.
Engine will not start	Flat battery, faulty starter	Push start or tow start. (Diesels very difficult to push start)
Engine overheating	Low coolant	Allow engine to fast idle with the bonnet up before turning off to allow cooling. Top up with coolant.
	Hose leak	Wrap plastic tape round hole and reinforce with wire. Remove radiator cap to reduce system pressure if necessary.

Broken fanbelt		Cord or tights/ stockings can be used but an emergency belt is much better.
Radiator or joint leak		Block holes with silicon rubber sealer or chewing gum. Close off leaking capillary tubes by crimping with pliers. Put in sealing compound: ie Radweld, porridge oats or even raw eggs or raw maize meal.
Sticking thermostat		Can be removed for short periods but this will affect water flow around engine and can give long term problems.

Note: Overheating can be reduced by turning on the heater in the vehicle to take heat away from the engine.

Transmission and Brakes

Unable to select/change gears	Clutch failure	Try clutchless gear changes. Adjust engine speed as gear lever is moved - higher revs to change down, lower revs to change up. The vehicle will start easily in first gear, low range.

No drive	Broken halfshaft	If rear shaft broken, remove and put gearbox in diff lock position.
		A failed front shaft is more difficult, but damage can be reduced by removing the front propshaft.
	Broken differential	Remove appropriate propshaft and, to reduce damage, remove driveshafts. Put the gearbox in differential lock and avoid using low range.
		Drive cautiously - avoid hard acceleration.
Brakes ineffective or 'pulling' to one side	Leaking wheel cylinder or brake line	To prevent further fluid loss, isolate the leak by crimping or folding the pipe. Drive slowly and avoid using the brakes if possible.

Tools and materials can also be improvised by using whatever is available to you:

- A worm-drive clip of 100mm diameter makes an effective piston ring compressor.

- If you suspect an engine cylinder of poor compression, remove the injector and pour in some diesel fuel. Remove the sump. Replace the injector and turn the crankshaft until the piston is in the compression position. Check at sump end for 'leaked' diesel fuel (If the cylinder is worn or oval shaped, this may take several minutes).

- The Land Rover pillar jack makes a good chassis spreader when removing the gear box cross member. Used with chains, it can become a basic but effective body puller.

- If you have no wire for lashing parts together or for use as improvised cables, burn your old scrap tyres and use the steel bracing.

- Engine power can be roughly measured by assessing performance when driving up hill or through deep sand and comparing with experience of good performance under similar conditions.

- Emergency puncture repairs can be carried out without patches or replacement tubes by stuffing tyres with rags or grass. Tyres must be discarded after use in this way.

- A cylinder block that is cracked between the bores can be repaired by drilling small vertical holes in the crack and plugging with steel screws so that the barbs flatten. File off flush.

3.K EMERGENCY ACTION - IF YOU BECOME STRANDED

If your vehicle is beyond even improvised repairs because of exceptionally serious damage or because it is trapped

DON'T PANIC – STAY CALM – CONSERVE YOUR ENERGY – ALWAYS STAY WITH THE VEHICLE – CONCENTRATE ON ATTRACTING ASSISTANCE.

Heliographs or ordinary mirrors, whistles and signal flares are effective ways of attracting the attention of pilots and vehicle drivers.

You can survive without food for some time, depending on your general health and physique but **water is essential.**

REMEMBER - Always carry sufficient emergency water and check that it is drinkable before setting out.

Avoid exposure to fierce sunlight to prevent dehydration. Use your Land Rover as a shade or construct one using a blanket, tarpaulin or the bonnet of your Land Rover which can be removed without spanners.

If possible, turn the vehicle to take advantage of any breeze which can cool the interior. Never lie under the vehicle if the ground is soft as the vehicle may sink down.

1. SEARCH AND RESCUE BEACONS

New systems, products and improvements are continuously being introduced. For latest information on what is available, contact specialist suppliers, or the Royal Geographical Society, 1, Kensington Gore, London SW7 2AR, England, UK.

Telephone: 44 (0) 20 7591 3000 Fax: 44 (0) 20 7591 3001

Website: www.rgs.org

2. EMERGENCIES - FURTHER READING

In this handbook:

Phonetic Alphabet	Section 7.A
International Ground/Air Distress Code	Section 7.B
Visual body signals	Section 7.B
High ambient - wind heat	Section 7.D
Solar load	Section 7.E
Human water needs v temperature	Section 7.H
Days of expected survival	Section 7.H
Independent Publications	Section 7.M

Books in print vary from day to day and we recommend that you consult the Royal Geographical Society - details on previous page, amazon.com, landrover.com and brooklands-books.com for the latest relevant publications.

4. WHAT FUEL?

4. FUEL FACTS

CONTENTS
PART ONE

PART TWO - IN DEPTH

4.A FUEL - HOW MUCH DO YOU NEED?

The table below shows how much diesel fuel you might expect to use - in miles per gallon or litres per 100km - but these are only guidelines. Consumption can vary depending on the driver, type of terrain and vehicle.

Fuel use estimates can be based on one driver's performance, using the brim-to-brim method - fill up the tank, drive for a set distance and then refill to the brim from a measure-marked container. Consumption can then be calculated.

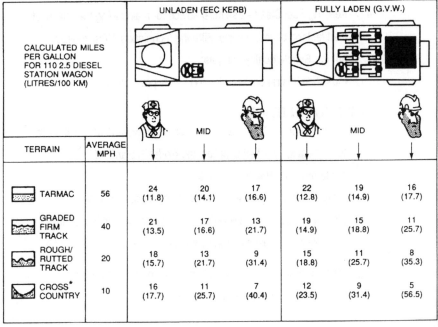

CALCULATED MILES PER GALLON FOR 110 2.5 DIESEL STATION WAGON (LITRES/100 KM)		UNLADEN (EEC KERB)			FULLY LADEN (G.V.W.)		
TERRAIN	AVERAGE MPH		MID			MID	
TARMAC	56	24 (11.8)	20 (14.1)	17 (16.6)	22 (12.8)	19 (14.9)	16 (17.7)
GRADED FIRM TRACK	40	21 (13.5)	17 (16.6)	13 (21.7)	19 (14.9)	15 (18.8)	11 (25.7)
ROUGH/ RUTTED TRACK	20	18 (15.7)	13 (21.7)	9 (31.4)	15 (18.8)	11 (25.7)	8 (35.3)
CROSS* COUNTRY	10	16 (17.7)	11 (25.7)	7 (40.4)	12 (23.5)	9 (31.4)	5 (56.5)

LITRES/100 KM = 100 + (MPG X 0.354)

REMEMBER - Though the figures above include an assumed amount of hill climbing, extra mountainous regions will increase consumption, as will extra loads.

NOTE: EEC Kerb weight includes the standard vehicle, a driver and a full fuel load.

* 'Cross country' does not indicate all terrain more severe than rough rutted tracks - some conditions cannot be predicted.

HOW TO CALCULATE FUEL CONSUMPTION

If One Land Rover 110 Diesel's expected (intensive use) mileage per month = 1500 miles.

Terrain (Dry Season) Rough Track with fully laden vehicle driven by average drivers = 11 mpg (see table).

Monthly consumption = 1500 divided by 11 = 136 gallons or 3 x 45 gallon drums (approx).

Annual consumption = 12 x 136 = 1632 gallons or 36 x 45 gallon drums.

REMEMBER - If fuel is scarce, buying it locally in this quantity is likely to push up the price. Look for a volume source closer to the oil company.

In the absence of fuel stations, the responsibility for fuel lies with you.

Petrol is a heavy responsibility, demanding expensive and complicated underground storage. **It remains a serious fire risk at all times.**

Diesel can be stored overground safely even in ambient temperatures over 50°C.

DRUM STORAGE (205 litres) or JERRY CAN (20 litres)

In our experience, drums are a troublesome way of receiving fuel, especially if the containers are old and contaminated - see Section 4.E. Jerry cans, being smaller, simply multiply the problem because you need more of them.

TANK STORAGE

Gasoline tanks must go underground and they need special dispensing pumps. See an expert. Gasoline deteriorates quickly under high ambient temperatures so deliveries must be smaller and more frequent.

Diesel can be stored safely. Even in temperatures consistently higher than 30°C will not deteriorate for at least six months - so two deliveries a year may be sufficient.

Installing and maintaining storage tanks - see Sections 4.G.

REMEMBER - All fuel is potentially dangerous. Keep it away from people, buildings and drinking water sources.

4.C PUMPING FUEL - WHAT PUMP FOR DRUMS?

All handpumps involve hard and unrewarding work. This can be avoided, in the case of diesel, with a gravity-feed overground tank.

If there is no alternative, select a rotary-action hand-operated drum pump with a pipe that can be adjusted to draw fuel from just above the bottom of the drum.

DRUM STORE LOCATION

Store the drums so you can take the vehicles to them, not the other way round. Moving the drums disturbs sediment which can be transferred into the vehicle's tank.

Ferrying the fuel by jerry can from the drum to the vehicle is just as bad - it is tiring, time-consuming and strictly for people who want the extra exercise.

A fill-up using jerry cans can take up to 30 minutes. Pouring diesel from an overground tank direct into the vehicle's tank through a filtered funnel is easier, cleaner and takes half the time.

Filtering is essential - and even an old (but clean) cotton shirt can trap the water and dirt particles that could eventually bring your Land Rover to a halt.

Choose a funnel with a built-in fine copper mesh - 'holes' no bigger than 63 microns (mesh size 210) are best - and make sure it is big enough to avoid spillage under normal filling.

REMEMBER - Watch for high sulphur levels in Diesel fuel available outside Europe. Excessive sulphur rapidly deteriorates engine oil which could lead to engine damage.

If the sulphur level is 1% by weight or above, the condition of the oil must be monitored regularly. Check the oil's condition regularly and change as often as necessary. There are no warning signs. The sudden thickening of the oil which signals oil fatigue occurs after the damage has been done.

Ask your local supplier for sulphur level details or send a sample for laboratory analysis.

1. CLEAN FUEL - DON'T FORGET. . .

Drum storage of fuels calls for a high standard of care from all personnel involved. Insist that the Drum Code in Section 4. E. is strictly followed.

TANK storage enables you to closely control the care, filtering and dispensing of the fuel. See Section 4.G.

2. SECURITY AND ADMINISTRATION

Fuel is expensive to buy and easy to sell at a local market! Protect your interests by dip-measuring your supplies regularly. Locks on tanks and stores prevent accidents as well as losses. Appoint an official fuel dispenser and insist only he/she does the job - drivers in a hurry are likely to bend the rules.

3. SAFETY

In the event of a fuel fire, never use water in attempts to control the flames. Water turns to steam which spreads the blaze.

REMEMBER - Water + Oil/Fuel Fire = Dangerous Fire Ball.

Smother the flames with earth or sand. Flames on people can be extinguished by rolling them in a blanket.

4.E STORING DRUMS (FUEL, OILS AND GREASES)

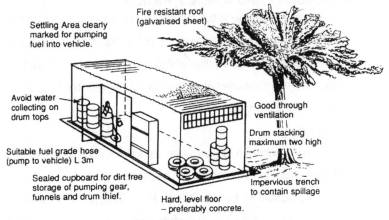

Settling Area clearly marked for pumping fuel into vehicle.

Fire resistant roof (galvanised sheet)

Avoid water collecting on drum tops

Good through ventilation

Drum stacking maximum two high

Suitable fuel grade hose (pump to vehicle) L 3m

Sealed cupboard for dirt free storage of pumping gear, funnels and drum thief.

Impervious trench to contain spillage

Hard, level floor – preferably concrete.

4 old tyres for unloading drums outside store. (Better to roll drums down stout plank if available)

Minimum size of suitable building (15 Drums not stacked) H 3m W 3m L 3m

Minimum access for Land Rovers outside building H 2.5m W 3m L 5m

Minimum door width for drum delivery and pumping 1.5m

Minimum settling time for drums 3 hours.

WARNING

Do not site drum store where accidental spillage could result in contamination of water supply or human/animal habitation.

Any fuel, oil and lubricant store is an area of high fire risk – please take the necessary no smoking, no naked flame, no spark precautions.

1. EQUIPMENT FOR DRUM STORE

Gloves for protection from fuel.

Spanner to open/close drums.

Drum thief (tube for sampling fuel).

Drum pumps with fitted discharge hoses – one per type of fuel, oil or lubricant.

Large filter funnels – one for each type of fuel, oil or lubricant.

3m discharge flexible hoses for drum to vehicle pumping – one for each type.

Drum calibrated dip stick.

Fuel and oil resistant marking paint for drums.

Large good quality padlocks for securing store.

Cupboard suitable for storing above.

Old vehicle tyres for drum dropping or stout planks.

Fire extinguisher suitable for products stored (Personnel must be trained how to use it!) See section 7.I for details.

2. THE DRUM CODE

1. WEAR gloves. Don't Smoke.

2. KEEP all drums tightly sealed except when drawing fuel.

3. STORE drums in secure but ventilated area out of sun.

4. MARK all drums with paint to show contents and date of purchase. Use oldest drums first.

5. CLEAN and dry drums before opening to avoid contamination. Open hot containers slowly to avoid pressure spillage.

6. CHECK the quality and purity of EACH drum before vehicle filling. Use a Drum Thief (See Section 4.F)

7. AVOID pumping direct from the bottom of a drum - dirt collects here.

8. PUMP fuel through a clean filter funnel approved to British Standard 410 (Mesh size 210 / 63 micron). If not available, improvise with a clean cotton shirt.

9. NEVER put petrol in a diesel engine vehicle's tank or diesel in a petrol engined vehicle.

10. ALWAYS use separate pumps, funnels and filters for different fluids. Mark all items clearly.

SUGGESTED SYMBOLS FOR MARKING DRUMS ETC. – WHERE READING PRESENTS DIFFICULTIES		
GASOLINE (PETROL)	▲	RED
DIESEL	■	YELLOW
BRAKE/CLUTCH FLUID	●	BLUE
GEARBOX OIL (ATF)	★	GREEN
TRANSFER BOX AND AXLE OIL	◓	BLACK

3. GENERAL NOTES ON USING DRUMS

1. Handling Drums

Wear gloves. Full drums are heavy so roll them off lorries down a stout plank or, if there is no alternative, use old tyres to cushion the cautious drop from the vehicle. Careful, or drums may dent or split.

2. **Water Contamination**

Accidentally or deliberately, water sometimes gets into fuel drums. Even aviation fuel has fallen victim to this, so check each drum's contents before accepting its delivery.

3. **Dip Measurement**

Improvise a no-spark risk dipstick from a broom handle or any hardwood or brass stick, calibrated with marks (18mm equals 1 gallon). A full drum's level should reach about 30mm from the top.

REMEMBER - A dented drum holds less than a perfectly cylindrical drum.

4. **Fuel 'Setting' and Sampling**

Allow three hours for the disturbed contents of a moved drum to settle. (See section 4.F for simple purity testing.)

Rough guide: allow one hour per foot of fuel depth in tanks.

5. **Old Drums**

If fuel is delivered in old drums, check marks and codes to establish previous contents. For example, old glue residue can inflict damage on fuel systems.

6. **Health and Safety**

Protect your skin from contact with diesel or gasoline. Long term exposure may pose a serious health risk. Wash with soap and water. Always wear gloves.

Avoid accidental swallowing or inhalation of diesel. If small amount swallowed, do not induce vomiting as breathing in the fumes can be more damaging than the risk of poisoning. Seek medical advice immediately.

4.F SIMPLE FUEL PURITY TESTING & HOME-MADE 'DRUM THIEF'

Straightforward and reliable testing of fuels can be carried out simply with a length of PVC tubing and two widely available scientific instruments - the nose and the eye! Add a litre measure and a set of scales and the 'laboratory' is complete.

It helps if you have previously familiarised yourself with the sight and aroma of fuel you know to be good.

1. TAKING A SAMPLE

Liquids that contaminate fuels will have different densities to the fuel itself - and that means heavier ones will sink to the bottom while lighter ones will stay towards the top. This is why tipping out some of the contents is no accurate guide to what is inside.

Take out a top-to-bottom 'section' by dipping in the tube to the bottom, place your thumb over the top and withdraw the tube. A complete level-by-level sample will be contained in it.

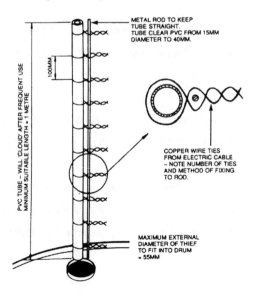

METAL ROD TO KEEP
TUBE STRAIGHT.
TUBE CLEAR PVC FROM 15MM
DIAMETER TO 40MM.

100MM

PVC TUBE - WILL 'CLOUD' AFTER FREQUENT USE
MINIMUM SUITABLE LENGTH - 1 METRE

COPPER WIRE TIES
FROM ELECTRIC CABLE
- NOTE NUMBER OF TIES
AND METHOD OF FIXING
TO ROD.

MAXIMUM EXTERNAL
DIAMETER OF THIEF
TO FIT INTO DRUM
- 55MM

2. ANALYSING YOUR SAMPLE

1. Release the contents into a clear glass container - an empty Whisky bottle is ideal! - and check for visual clues.

2. Smell the sample and then, after shaking the sample, smell it again. Check for differences.

3. If possible, weigh exactly one litre of the sample - see Section 7.K for densities chart.

Taking and analysing a sample from a drum (205L)

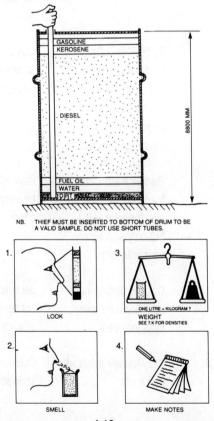

NB. THIEF MUST BE INSERTED TO BOTTOM OF DRUM TO BE A VALID SAMPLE. DO NOT USE SHORT TUBES.

1. LOOK

3. ONE LITRE = KILOGRAM ? WEIGHT SEE 7.K FOR DENSITIES

2. SMELL

4. MAKE NOTES

3. DIESEL FUEL CONTAMINATION TEST CHART

CONTAMINANT	CONSEQUENCES	TEST METHOD
WATER	Damage to pump and injectors. Rapid rusting - possibly overnight.	Visual inspection of sample of settled fuel. Water seen as clear separate layer.
FOREIGN BODIES (DIRT)	Damage to pump and injectors - possible pump seizure.	Large particles seen at bottom of sample - small particles can be filtered out. No loss of smell.
GASOLINE (Petrol)	FIRE RISK - 2% contamination makes diesel as hazardous as neat petrol. Poor hot start - damage to pistons.	Gasoline less dense so settles on top - strong petrol smell .
KEROSENE (Paraffin)	Reduced lubrication leads to pump and injector wear - but only with heavy contamination.	Can only be detected by weight/density check.
FUEL OIL (Boiler)	Causes carbon build-up in injectors and cylinder head .	Jet black colour contamination - no change in smell.
OXIDISATION	Only heavily oxidised fuel a risk.	Colour darkens - acrid smell.

4. PHYSICAL DATA

In order of increasing density (for actual values see section 7.K)

GASOLINE (Petrol) - Volatile, highly inflammable vapour. Light straw colour with distinct smell.

KEROSENE (Paraffin) - Non-volatile, light straw colour with smell similar to Diesel fuel.

DIESEL - Non-volatile, light straw colour with pungent smell.

FUEL OILS (Boiler Fuel) - Non-volatile, black in colour with smell similar to Diesel.

FOREIGN BODIES (Dirt) - Solid, generally heavier than liquids, so deposits at lowest levels.

4.G DIESEL STORAGE TANKS

DANGER - The storage of Gasoline in small, vented overground tanks is a major fire risk.

The tank system described here is as widely used by European farmers and for storage of domestic heating oil.

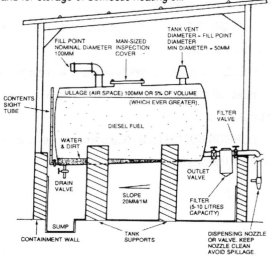

1. TANK INSTALLATION AND CONSTRUCTION

1. SELECTING A SITE

Remember the tank must be accessible for tanker deliveries and for vehicle dispensing - it will need a walled containment area at least 10 per cent bigger than the tank itself to limit spillage - if wall not possible, ensure that spillage poses no risk to water supply or people.

2. TANK SHAPE AND MATERIAL

The tank can be either cylindrical or rectangular, with a welded mild steel construction. Do not use galvanised steel, low grade alloys or natural rubber. Ensure adequate plate thickness for size of tank.

3. **FUEL FILTER**

Fit a suitable wire mesh filter to the discharge point. These are commercially available from fuel station suppliers. For diesel fuels, the mesh size should be 63 micron (0.063mm) or 240 size to British Standard 410. Fit a filter with a large capacity (5-10 litres) to cater for contaminated fuels. Avoid using too-fine filters - they will clog up too often and cause slow filling.

4. **PIPE RUNS**

Ensure that pipe-runs are as short as possible, self draining, won't sag and are protected if underground.

5. **FIREFIGHTING EQUIPMENT**

Always have adequate fire extinguishing equipment available with a trained operator when filling or draining a storage tank.

6. **COLD WEATHER**

Diesel fuel forms wax globules at temperatures below freezing. Diesel obtained in hot regions is unlikely to contain anti-waxing additives so beware of storing diesel at high altitude where night temperatures fall dramatically.

2. SIMPLE GOOD HOUSEKEEPING
Weekly Tasks

1. Drain water and sludge from bottom of tank - especially during any rains.

2. Remove and clean filter basket on dispensing hose.

3. Check stock against consumption using dipstick or sight glass and comparing with vehicle log sheets.

Monthly Tasks. (In addition to weekly tasks)

1. Take a sample of fuel from dispensing nozzle and check for purity and/or oxidisation.

2. Check tank vent for blockage.

3. Check all pipe unions and valves for drips, corrosion or cracking.

4. If tank is installed within containment wall - remove rainwater from sump.

5. WHICH WORKSHOP?

5. WHICH WORKSHOP?

CONTENTS
PART ONE

PART TWO – IN DEPTH

5.A INTRODUCTION
– WHY DO I NEED A WORKSHOP?

A workshop is not an expensive luxury. For the purposes for which it is intended here, it is simply an area where work can be carried out to keep a Land Rover in good condition - anywhere.

It can be as simple as a patch of hard, level ground for a driver/mechanic and his toolbox. It can be a structure for the continuous care of a whole fleet of vehicles.

Though it may seem a bold step to take, in the absence of a local distributor it would be the only way of ensuring efficient vehicle operation for projects of six months duration or more.

REMEMBER - preventive maintenance is the key to reliable operation of your Land Rover.

The workshop must fit the needs of your fleet. If it is too small, the work overload will result in delays in getting vehicles back on the road. If it is too big, it will be under-used. This section should help.

REMEMBER - Try and keep your workshop size flexible to allow your fleet to grow.

Mobile workshops should be considered only if your operation is to be nomadic. Contact Land Rover Special Vehicle Operations at Solihull for details.

For ease of planning, select the fleet size plan which includes your vehicle fleet numbers. If the fleet size exceeds 15 vehicles, consider opening a second facility - possibly in another location if the area covered is large.

MODULE 1. 1 - 2 VEHICLES

A basic single-vehicle workshop for this operation could be close to your accommodation. A concrete floor is easy to keep clean but 'rammed' earth can offer a cheap but effective working surface.

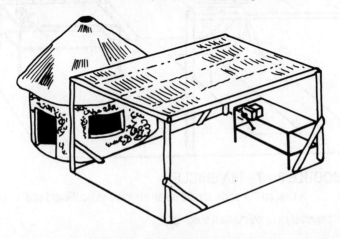

The area should be drained on three sides with access on the 'downhill' side. In dry hot areas, a simple shade will keep the sun off but permit cooling breezes. Roll-down canvas sides may be useful against windblown dust. In wet areas, a larger, more substantial shelter will be needed. (See section 5.G.)

In both cases, tools should be stored in secure, lockable boxes.

MODULE 2. 3 - 6 VEHICLES
This can be of similar design to the 1-2 vehicle plan, but with a work area twice the size so that two vehicles can be worked on together. One half could be equipped with a pit for vehicle inspection and maintenance, though the potential drainage problem may make a brick ramp construction a better option. (See section 5.J.)

MODULE 3. 7 - 15 VEHICLES
A fleet on this scale should be an effective self-sufficient unit, preferably in a permanent building.

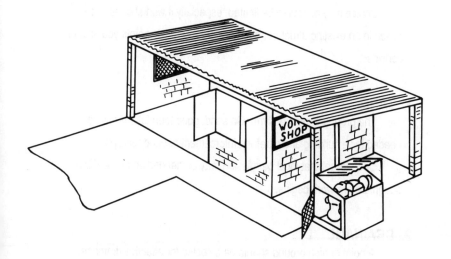

It should include:

1. A ramp or pit area under cover.
2. Flat work area under cover.
3. Flat hardstanding outside.
4. Office - for administration.
5. Stores area - for spares, tools etc.
6. Machine shop - bench driller, hydraulic press, welding area etc.
7. Generator room - positioned to avoid noise problem
8. Vehicle wash down area.
9. Fuel storage - see section 4.H for drums and 4.J for tanks.
10. Fenced compound with access gates.
11. Security guard accommodation.
12. Ablution block - toilet, shower etc.

For a typical design, see section 5.K.

5.C WORKSHOP LOCATION

Choice may of course be limited, especially if workshop is to be based in an existing structure, but there are four basic points you should consider:

1. LAND

The ground should be firm. On sand, good foundations will be needed for a building and careful reinforcement needed for a pit.

Don't forget that local permission may be needed and should be sought before work begins.

2. DRAINAGE

A point of high ground should be selected for effective drainage. Any drainage ditches should self-drain or run to a 'soak-away'. Ensure that no pollution of water sources can be caused.

3. LOCATION

Remember that your workshop will cause noise and fumes so position it to avoid upsetting local inhabitants and livestock. But don't forget that an over-remote workshop will be a security risk.

4. ACCESS

The workshop should offer easy access for the people and vehicles it is there to serve.

5.D WORKSHOP EQUIPMENT
– WHAT WILL YOU NEED?

This is an outline list of the equipment you should consider, depending on the workshop size. See Section 5.L for a detailed list.

Module 1. 1-2 Vehicles
Work bench and vice

Axle stands

Assorted tools and box

Parts box

Fuel/oil funnels and drain tins

Fuel drum pump - (See Section 4.F)

Module 2. 3-6 Vehicles
Module 1 Equipment plus:

Trolley jack

Additional bench

Increased Parts storage

'Shadow' board for tools

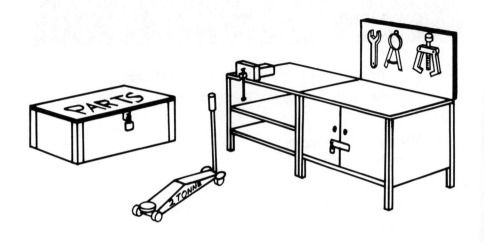

Module 3. 7-15 Vehicles

Module 1 & 2 equipment plus:

Minimum two benches with vices

Tyre changing machine

Racking for tools and parts stores area

Generator and air compressor

Hydraulic press

Distribution board and fusebox

Portable welding gear

Hoist

Bench driller and grinder

Hand held cutter/grinder

Fuel storage and distribution

Racking for tyres

Pit with cover or Ramp

Office Equipment

Fire extinguisher(s)

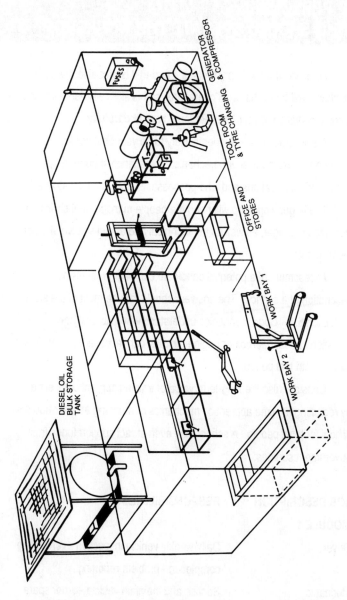

For a more detailed list, see 5.K and 5.L. For details on fuel drum storage or tank storage, see Sections 4.H and 4.J respectively. For fire extinguisher details, see Section 7.I.

For a small workshop (Modules 1 and 2) it is probable that your mechanic will be in charge of operations, so his skills will determine the running condition of your Land Rovers - **recruit carefully.**

A self sufficient all-rounder is likely to be your best option - someone whose skills cover mechanical experience supported by vocational qualifications and who possesses simple administrative skills.

The larger workshop will need the people management skills of a workshop manager, as well as the technical and administrative skills of the workshop.

Assessment of a potential candidate can begin with his/her description of a service. The answers should include most of the steps in Section 5.N. Good mechanics understand why - not just how. Questions about gearbox or engine function can reveal a lot. Consider a three month trial period.

Consider also the long-term value of training apprentices - either by recruiting full-time apprentice mechanics or runnning an after-hours school for local people. A school may even attract support funds from government sources.

JOB DESCRIPTION	RESPONSIBILITIES
MODULE 1	
Driver	Daily/weekly vehicle inspection - vehicle log completion - problem reporting.
Mechanic	Service and maintain vehicle - order spare parts - dispense fuel and monitor use - vehicle administration (including vehicle records, ordering of fuel and spares stock).

MODULE 2

Driver (per vehicle)	As Module 1.
Mechanic	Service and maintain vehicles.
Administrator	Maintain vehicle, spares and fuel logs. Allocate vehicles and monitor use.

MODULE 3

Driver (per vehicle)	As Modules 1 & 2.
Mechanic	As Module 2 + Train Assistant Mechanics.
Assistant Mechanic	As directed by Mechanic.
Workshop Manager	Supervise allocation of vehicles - Process administration and requests i.e. fuel and spares etc - Set priorities of workload - Overall control of workshop.
Storeman	Issue spare parts and tools - dispense fuel.
Guard	Patrol workshop and vehicle compound when closed.

Administration takes time but is vital for efficient operation. The use of a single log card per vehicle can keep the burden to a minimum if used correctly.

The key areas to be covered are:

Fuel/oil consumption, parts used and servicing details.

For a guideline design for a log card, see section 5.M. The majority of necessary information can be indicated on this. If the personnel involved have reading/writing difficulties, assisted logging may have to be used.

The log card is kept with the vehicle for collation and filing at the end of each month. A second copy of the card should be kept at the workshop, updated as required. Use the card to monitor the use and condition of tools carried with the vehicle.

1. FUEL AND SPARES

A dual purpose log card could be issued to the personnel responsible for issuing fuel/oil and spare parts. This would also show current stock held and parts on order. See Section 5.M for a sample card.

2. VEHICLE CONDITION

In addition to the vehicle log card, consider using a wall-mounted 'vehicle status' board on which vehicle information can be clearly shown, ie: date, driver, destination, next service etc.

Drivers can be reminded of 'service due' dates and/or mileages with a label attached to the dashboard or speedometer.

3. TOOLS

Records of tool loan from the stores should be logged in and out. 'Shadow' type tool mounting boards which clearly show which tools are out on loan are useful. Mechanics should sign for or hand over a token to acknowledge possession.

4. FIRE PREVENTION

Untidy workshops can be a fire risk. Personnel should be aware of the need to clear rubbish and rags - particularly oil-soaked rags - and be trained in basic fire fighting techniques - see Section 7.I Fire Fighting for details. A strict 'no smoking' ban should be enforced in and around the workshop - and this should include cooking stoves. Welding and gasoline tank draining must never take place at the same time.

GROUND PREPARATION AND DRAINAGE

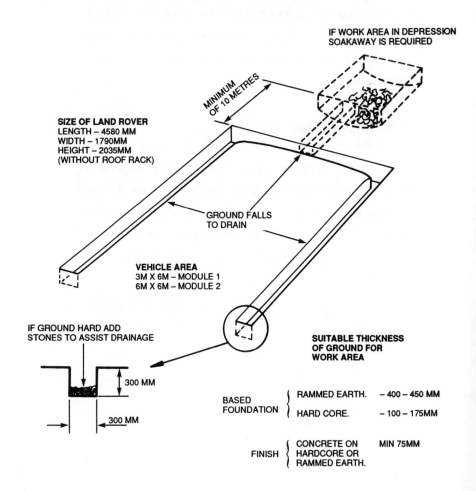

IF WORK AREA IN DEPRESSION
SOAKAWAY IS REQUIRED

MINIMUM OF 10 METRES

SIZE OF LAND ROVER
LENGTH – 4580 MM
WIDTH – 1790MM
HEIGHT – 2035MM
(WITHOUT ROOF RACK)

GROUND FALLS
TO DRAIN

VEHICLE AREA
3M X 6M – MODULE 1
6M X 6M – MODULE 2

IF GROUND HARD ADD
STONES TO ASSIST DRAINAGE

300 MM

300 MM

**SUITABLE THICKNESS
OF GROUND FOR
WORK AREA**

BASED
FOUNDATION
{ RAMMED EARTH.   – 400 – 450 MM
HARD CORE.   – 100 – 175MM

FINISH
{ CONCRETE ON   MIN 75MM
HARDCORE OR
RAMMED EARTH.

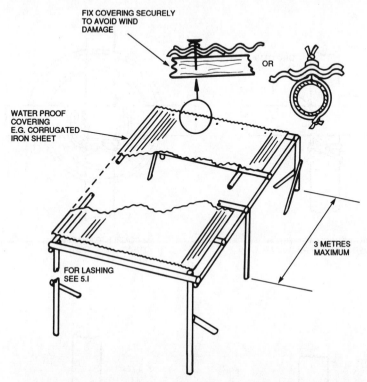

FIX COVERING SECURELY TO AVOID WIND DAMAGE

OR

WATER PROOF COVERING E.G. CORRUGATED IRON SHEET

3 METRES MAXIMUM

FOR LASHING SEE 5.I

ANTI-LIFT AND LEAN FEET FOR SUPERIOR STRENGTH

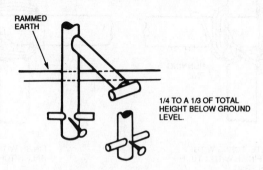

RAMMED EARTH

1/4 TO A 1/3 OF TOTAL HEIGHT BELOW GROUND LEVEL.

1

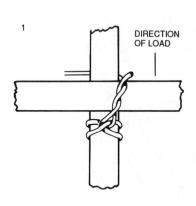

DIRECTION OF LOAD

START WITH CLOVE – HITCH
UNDER LOAD-BEARING SPAR.

3

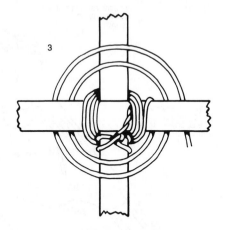

2 COMPLETE FRAPPING
TURNS. PULL TIGHT
AND BEAT IN!

2

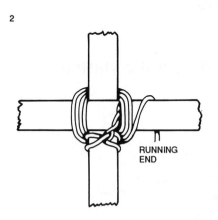

RUNNING END

4 COMPLETE TURNS WITH
LASHING. FINISH WITH 1 TURN
ON CROSS SPAR.

4

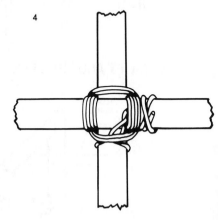

FINISH WITH TWO
HALF HITCHES.

5.J PIT CONSTRUCTION WORKSHOP MODULES 2 AND 3

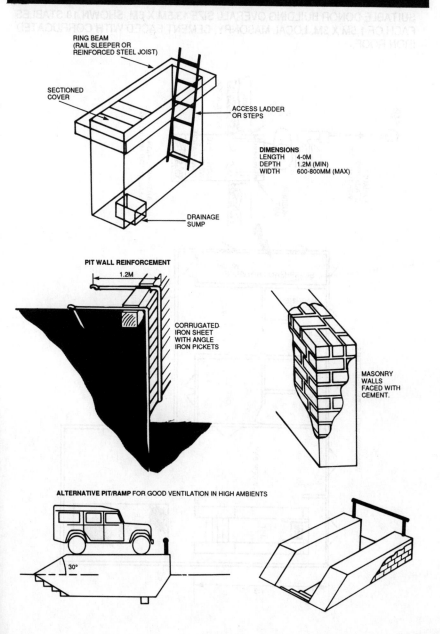

RING BEAM
(RAIL SLEEPER OR
REINFORCED STEEL JOIST)

SECTIONED
COVER

ACCESS LADDER
OR STEPS

DIMENSIONS
LENGTH   4-0M
DEPTH   1.2M (MIN)
WIDTH   600-800MM (MAX)

DRAINAGE
SUMP

PIT WALL REINFORCEMENT

1.2M

CORRUGATED
IRON SHEET
WITH ANGLE
IRON PICKETS

MASONRY
WALLS
FACED WITH
CEMENT.

ALTERNATIVE PIT/RAMP FOR GOOD VENTILATION IN HIGH AMBIENTS

30°

SUITABLE DONOR BUILDING OVERALL SIZE 13.5M X 6M. SHOWN 18 STABLES
EACH OF 1,5M X 3M. LOCAL MASONRY, CEMENT FACED WITH CORRUGATED
IRON ROOF.

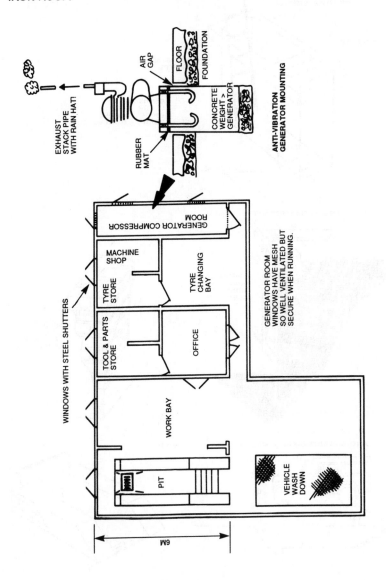

5.L VEHICLE AND WORKSHOP TOOLKITS

The following is a suggested list of tools to carry 'in vehicle' when operating out of an established base. The size and scope of the kit depends on the anticipated duration and distance of travel and the mechanical skill of the driver. This is not intended as an expedition list.

1. VEHICLE TOOL KIT
To be carried in addition to standard Land Rover tool kit.

Tool bag containing:
Combination spanner set 6 - 24mm.
Posidrive and flat blade screw drivers.
Roll of soft wire - insulated.
Roll of stainless steel wire 16 to 18 swg - for improvised repairs.
Two 18" (460mm) tyre levers.
Puncture Repair Kit - vulcanised patches and adhesive ('Hot patch' type).
30 metres of 25mm polypropylene or similar man-made fibre cord for recovery etc.
Pulley block - for use with cordage or winch.
12v battery operated lead light - clip or cigar socket termination depending on vehicle.
Large roll PVC insulating tape.

Optional Equipment:

Either:

12v mini tyre inflator.

(A small inflator tested took 25 minutes to inflate a 7.50 x 16 radial to 30psi (2.14 Bar) so check suitability of inflator.)

Or:

Foot or hand-pump - faster but labour intensive.

Large jack base plate for soft sand (400mm x 400mm x 2.5mm up to 5mm) in aluminium.

Consider also precaution parts which may be required depending on local conditions: spare fan belt, inner tube etc. (see section 2.C & 2.D)

2. WORKSHOP TOOL KIT

The following would be required in addition to a basic mechanics' or fitters' kit. Part numbers refer to special tools available from Land Rover merchandising service. See Land Rover publications list in Section 7.M for details.

Good quality handtools - your choice of manufacturer:

Combination spanners	– 6 to 24 mm.	
(Ring and open)	– 5/16" to 1 1/4" AF.	
Socket Sets	– 8 to 32 mm	1/2" Drive.
	– 5/16" to 1 1/4"	1/2" Drive.
	– 1/4" to 9/16"	3/8" Drive.
	– 6 to 10mm	3/8" Drive.
Socket Ratchets	– 1/2" and 3/8" Drive.	

Socket Extensions	– 2", 6" and 10"	1/2" Drive.
	– 2", 4" and 6"	3/8" Drive.
Knuckle Bar	– 3' long	1/2" Drive.
Socket adaptors		
(male type ends)	– 1/2" to 3/4" (for crank pulley).	
	– 1/2" to 3/8" (for cam belt tensioner).	
Socket	– 42mm (for crank pulley nut) 3/4" Drive.	
Torque wrench	– 0 to 150 ft/lbs click stop type best.	
Hammer	1lb and 2lb ball and pein.	
Mallet	Dual headed copper/nylon.	
Screwdrivers	Flat and Posidrive.	
Filter Wrench	Strap or chain type.	

Pop rivet gun and selection of 1/8" - 3/16" rivets.

Set of high speed twist drills - 1/16" to 1/2".

Two speed hand drill.

Punches - set from 2mm to 10mm diameter.

Tap and die set - standard metric threads.

Tyre levers - 18".

Feeler gauges - metric and Imperial.

Multimeter - Volts, Amps, Ohms (accurate down to 0.5 Ohms) supplied with leads and protective case.

3. LAND ROVER SPECIAL TOOLS

Wheel bearing box spanner - 2 1/16" AF.

Cranked socket extension	Pt No 606445 (to remove cylinder head without removing all injector assemblies).
Diesel DPS pump timing tool	– Pt No 18 G 1458
Camshaft and crankshaft gear remover	– Pt No 18 G 1463
DPS pump pulley extractor and retaining tool	– Pt No 18 G 1451/7
Gearbox bearing track puller	– Pt No 18 G 705/1
	– Pt No 18 G 705/1a

(Note: Cannot strip gearbox without it - the authors tried to improvise this tool for weeks without success!)

Two leg puller	– Pt No 18 G 1400

(May be improvised with hydraulic press)

Split collars x 2	– Pt No 18 G 705/1

(For layshaft bearing removal)

Split collar (for 5th gear removal)	– Pt No 18 G 1400-1

For a gearbox stripdown a press is essential if MS47 hand press is not available. (Other gearbox tools make job much easier but can be improvised).

4. FIELD WORKSHOP EQUIPMENT

The following is a guide to the equipment necessary for a Module 3 field workshop (7-15 vehicles).

REMEMBER - A first-time workshop in a remote area will need everything supplied, including easily overlooked essentials like electrical plugs and sockets, power cable, compressed air unions etc. An electric drill and a generator are useless unless you have the means to connect them!

Sundry additional equipment:

Water power wash - most are 240v, petrol or diesel 5/6bhp driven is better. Can be fed from an old oil drum. Typically 2,200 psi output at 15 litres/min.

Lengths of pressure hose for compressor ancillary equipment.

Extension cables for power tools, 15 Amp rating most durable.

Generator - 7.5 KVA 240 volt single or three phase, preferably diesel (4 KVA generator minimum for arc welding).

Compressor - portable petrol/diesel driven or static run by electric motor. Typical size - 15 cfm with a 50 litre reservoir - set to 50 psi max. line pressure. If in doubt of exact requirement, buy one size bigger.

In the vehicle bay:

4 Axle stands - 2 tonne capacity.

Hoist - 1.5 tonne capacity (crane if no roof beam support).

Trolley Jack - 2 tonne capacity (long reach useful).

Two 4" bench vices - benches may be made locally.

Lifting straps or chains - for use with hoist/crane.

Battery charger - heavy duty type with charge protection circuit. 15-20 Amp charge rate with 140 amp boost for vehicle starting.

Battery condition and vehicle charge tester (including rapid discharge facility).

Battery hydrometer.

Jump leads - minimum 3 metres long, 70 Amp (continuous) capacity for starting diesels.

In the tyre changing bay:

Tyre changing machine - light commercial (van and truck) type which uses compressed air to break seal of tyre bead on wheel rim. Ensure capacity for 7.50 x 16 tyres.

Schrader tyre inflator with built-in pressure gauge.

Tyre balancing machine (necessary only for Land Rovers mainly for on-road tarmac use).

In the machine shop:

Portable arc welder - to run off generator - 100 amp adjustable power for 1.5 to 2.5mm electrodes (beware voltage-drop problems over long cable runs).

Bench grinder - 125mm diameter wheels.

Bench pillar type driller - 1/2" chuck capacity with Morse taper location for larger chuck or drill bits. 5 speed 1/3rd HP motor suitable.

Portable hand drill - rechargeable type may be preferable - 1/2" chuck with two speeds.

Hand grinder - 4" wheels with stock of grinding/cutting wheels.

Hydraulic Press - 10 to 15 tonne capacity with adjustable height base.

1. SAMPLE LOG CARD

To keep paperwork to a minimum, the suggested log card could follow the format below (A4 size card - 280 gsm or similar).

Side One: Monthly Vehicle Usage

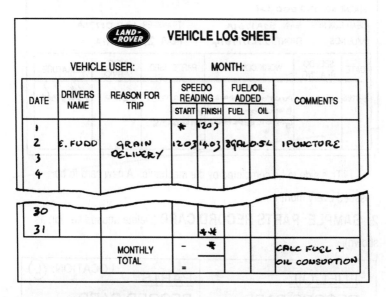

To be completed by the driver, with final calculations carried out be vehicle administrator.

Side Two: Monthly Service Record

VEHICLE LOG SHEET

LAND-ROVER

MONTHLY SERVICE RECORD

VEHICLE: 110 OOH 110Y   CHASSIS NO: 996333

ENGINE NO: 12J000836

GEAR BOX NOS MAIN: 50A1761A   TRANSFER: 12D 01771A

AXLE NOS   FRONT: 21L017814   REAR: 21501791A

DATE	SPEEDO READING	WORK COMPLETED	PARTS USED	NEXT SERVICE	SIGNATURE
2·5·86	1403	PUNTURE REPAIR BALL JOINT GATOR REPLACED	INNER TUBE GAITOR BTC 4198	2200	*Chrysmke*

This side to be completed by the mechanic. A new card to be
issued every month.

2. SAMPLE: PARTS RECORD CARD (Delete unused section as shown)

FUEL/OIL RECORD CARD	PARTS RECORD CARD LOCATION: (L)
FUEL TYPE: OIL TYPE:	PART NO: MUC 1031 DESCRIPTION DOOR LOCK ASSEMBLY

DATE	VEHICLE	ADDED TO STOCK	AMOUNT ISSUED	STOCK BALANCE	SIG
2·5·86	/	/	/	49	*Ponald Cork.*
4·5·86	110 – 117 OOH 110Y	/	2	47	*Mick Mouse*
5·5·86	110 – 96 AAM 90Y	/	1	46	*Elmu Fudd*

5-26

3. SAMPLE: FUEL/OIL RECORD CARD (Delete unused section as shown)

FUEL/OIL RECORD CARD FUEL TYPE: _DIESEL_ OIL TYPE: _N/A_			PARTS RECORD CARD PART NO: DESCRIPTION:		LOCATION:	
DATE	VEHICLE	ADDED TO STOCK	AMOUNT ISSUED	STOCK BALANCE	SIG	
2·5·86	✓	✓	✓	320 Liters	_David A Rook_	
3·5·86	110 – 117 OOH 110Y	✓	50L	270	_Mick Mouse_	
4·5·86	110 –96 AAH 90Y	✓	44L	226	_Elmo Fudd_	

4. SAMPLE: NEXT SERVICE REMINDER

DYMO TAPE ON FACIA:
NEXT SERVICE DUE 4000 km
OR ON 3.6.87

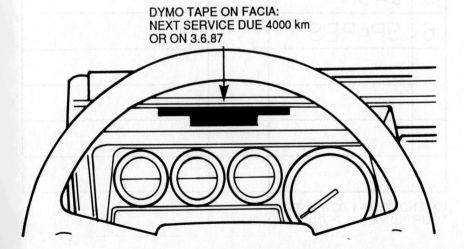

5. SAMPLE: VEHICLE ANCILLARY EQUIPMENT CHECK LIST

VEHICLE KIT
CHECK LIST
VEHICLE :

	ITEM	✓	COMMENTS
1	FIRST AID		
2	TOOLS		
3	TYRES		
4	PUNCTURE		
5	JACK		
6	SPARES		

EXTEND ITEMS 1 TO 6 TO SUIT
YOUR INDIVIDUAL REQUIREMENTS

5.N SIMPLE SERVICE SCHEDULE AS USED BY AUTHORS

A checklist of service items to carry out during a regular service ensures that nothing is overlooked. Land Rover's own service checklist, as supplied to Land Rover agents, covers all vehicle variants and is necessarily complex.

For the benefit of mechanics in remote areas, the drawing up of a simple at-a-glance schedule can simplify matters.

TWO MONTHLY OR 4000 km FIELD SERVICE SCHEDULE - LAND ROVER ONE TEN:

NB. 50,000 km hydraulic fluid change

40,000 km engine timing belt change
(for 2.5 Diesel engines up to 300TDi)

VIN: (Vehicle Identification No.)   SALLDHMC8BA 232853
Reg. No.   vs 4331
Engine No.   12J 09528
Date: 3.4.86
Speedometer reading: 10,931 km

Test drive checks

1. Selection of all 12 gears
2. Diff-lock operation - in and out
3. Steering - free play at wheel
4. Foot brake effectiveness
5. Transmission brake effectiveness
6. Instruments operation
7. Warning lights operation

8. Interior light

9. Exterior lamps

10. Wipers/washers - front and rear

11. Seat belts and seat mounting/covers

12. Wheel bearing free-play
    front LH/RH - rear LH/RH

13. Shock absorbers
    front LH/RH - rear LH/RH

14. Tyres
    front LH/RH - rear LH/RH
    + spares

15. Clutch operation

16. Door locks/window winders

17. Engine performance

Work for level ground

1. Check battery level - clean and grease connections

2. Lubricate accelerator pivot

3. Lubricate door locks and hinges

4. Rear brakes - strip, clean and adjust

Work with open bonnet

5. New fuel filter/sedimentor

6. Check fuel systems for leaks

7. Check brake fluid level

8. Check engine breather pipe

9. Check clutch fluid level

10. Check throttle operation

11. Check brake servo pipe

12. Check coolant level

13. Check washer level

14. Adjust tappet clearance

15. Heater plug wiring

16. Check oil cooler pipes

17. Check fan belt

18. Check air cleaner

19. Check coolant pipes and system

20. Bonnet adjustment

21. Roof rack security and accessories

Work for pit or ramp

1. Change engine oil and filter

2. Check steering damper for leaks. Check bushes

3. Check steering for damage/free-play

4. Check front suspension bushes and fixings

5. Check swivel pin housing oil level

6. Check front axle oil for leaks + breather security

7. Check front brake pads

8. Check wading plug and front cover

9. Check engine mountings for damage

10. Check front propshaft - UJ and bolts

11. Check gearbox oil

12. Check transfer box oil

13. Check exhaust for leaks and overall security

14. Check front chassis for damage

15. Check fore/aft brake + fuel lines for damage

16. Check rear suspension bushes and fixings

17. Check rear propshaft UJ and bolts

18. Check rear axle oil

19. Check rear brake lines for damage

20. Check fuel tank for damage

21. Check rear chassis for damage

6. WHICH EXTRAS?

6. WHICH EXTRAS?

CONTENTS

6.A INTRODUCTION

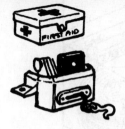

The 'Which Land Rover?' chapter tells you the questions you need to ask yourself in order to choose the right type of Land Rover for the job. This section covers how you can equip it to carry the job out more effectively.

6.B TOOLS AND EQUIPMENT

Choosing and compiling the right selection of tools and equipment depends on personal needs and local conditions.

In Section 5.L Vehicle Workshop Tool Kits we suggest a standard set of tools. This is designed as a compact and lightweight starting point to which 'special' tools can be added if necessary.

REMEMBER - an over-equipped tool kit can lead to over-ambitious repairs by under-skilled personnel. Make sure that tools for major jobs are available only to your workshop staff.

Land Rover factory-issue tool kits are stored behind the seats in pickups and under the right hand front seat in a station wagon (except those fitted with extra fuel tanks).

Additional tools and equipment can be stored for easy access in the 'cubby' box under the seat, reached by lifting the seat base and cover plate.

Protect tools and avoid annoying rattles by foam-padding the interior. Cleats for tying down tools with elasticated straps can be fitted.

Allocating a place for each tool and item of equipment means they are easier to find when you need them - and they can also be 'counted back in' when you have finished with them.

Items stored in the vented battery box under the left hand seat should be individually protected against dirt and water. Avoid storing metal items in the battery box that could accidentally short out the battery terminals.

EQUIPMENT CHECKLIST - SUGGESTED INCLUSIONS

Experience has shown that the following items make up an important basic extras kit:

12v Lead light - useful for nightwork or probing dark corners. Small and efficient fluorescent lights are available for direct temporary connection to the vehicle's battery with 'crocodile' clips or dashboard cigar lighter socket (optional on most Land Rovers).

Tow rope - Man-made fibre versions enable no-jolt, shock-absorbing towing. Choose one at least 25mm (1") in diameter. At least 30 metres of rope will be needed for vehicle recovery work. (Towing techniques - see section 6.D and 3.I.)

Pulley block - Useful for increasing pulling power of winch or recovery vehicle. See Section 6.D for use.

Jump leads - Make sure you obtain heavy duty leads with a continuous load capacity of 70 amps, capable of carrying the 200 amp short duration currents needed for jump starting. Not essential for all vehicles.

H-lift jack (Ratchet type) - Quicker to use than standard jack but needs care to avoid vehicle damage and possible injury to user through 'roll-offs' or sudden collapse while lowering. Can also be used as an emergency winch. **Not for the inexperienced.**

Jack base plate - Essential when jacking on soft ground to prevent sinking. A lightweight aluminium plate 400mm square by 2.5mm to 5mm minimum thick is ideal.

Shovel - for vehicle recovery and general use. Make sure the blade is 250mm (10") wide or less and is curved with pointed tip.

Canvas sheet - your temporary workshop floor. Can also double as a windbreak, especially on sandy soil which can frustrate puncture repairs with tiny abrasive fragments blown between tyre and tube. Should be at least 2 metres square.

Only the hi-lift jack will pose internal stowage problems. Consider mounting it on external brackets, retained with a padlock.

Further items of suggested equipment are included in the next sections.

6.C PUNCTURES

The risk of punctures during rough terrain driving are high. The risk can be reduced by ensuring correct tyre pressures and by avoiding obvious hazards, including sharp rocks, flints and large acacia-type thorns.

REMEMBER - Too-low pressures can lead to tyre slip on the rim which will tear the valve out of the inner tube.

1. USEFUL TYRE REPAIR EQUIPMENT

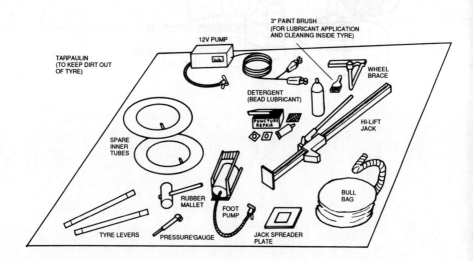

ALWAYS CHOCK WHEELS AND ENGAGE LOW RANGE AND DIFF LOCK BEFORE REMOVING A ROAD WHEEL.

2. BREAKING THE TYRE BEAD

USE THE LAND ROVER
JACK TO BREAK THE
BEAD ON A PUNCTURED
TYRE. BEAD CAN ALSO
BE BROKEN BY DRIVING
CAREFULLY OVER TYRE.

STRONG WOODEN
PACKING
(NOT BRICKS AS THEY
CAN CRUMBLE)

REMEMBER - If your Land Rover loses traction, first try reversing out - if the ground was good enough to get you there, it should be good enough to get you out.

Don't dig yourself into a hole by spinning the wheels - STOP. Lighten the vehicle by unloading passengers and cargo and get them to push. This is the quickest and surest way of recovering a vehicle.

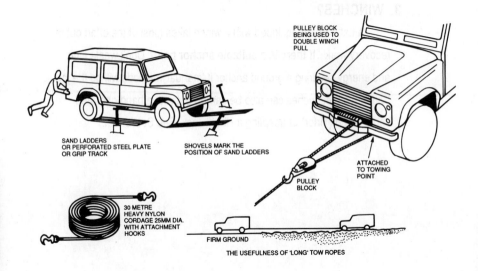

PULLEY BLOCK BEING USED TO DOUBLE WINCH PULL

SAND LADDERS OR PERFORATED STEEL PLATE OR GRIP TRACK

SHOVELS MARK THE POSITION OF SAND LADDERS

ATTACHED TO TOWING POINT

PULLEY BLOCK

30 METRE HEAVY NYLON CORDAGE 25MM DIA. WITH ATTACHMENT HOOKS

FIRM GROUND

THE USEFULNESS OF 'LONG' TOW ROPES

1. IF YOU ARE ALONE:

Dig a gentle ramp in front of each of the wheels. (Though not in sand - see over). If necessary lay brushwood, sacking etc in front of the wheels. If vehicle is up to axle level, jack up each corner in turn and 'fill in' hole and cover with thin brushwood* or even clothing if nothing else is available.

* Thick branches may damage vehicle during recovery.

2. ON SAND

Land Rovers that will be used on soft sand should be equipped with lightweight sand ladders. Aluminium is best but expensive - narrow perforated steel plate (PSP) is a reasonable compromise. Size: 170mm long, 250mm wide, 150mm rung spacing.

3. WINCHES?

A Land Rover equipped with a winch takes most of the effort out of recovery work - **If there is a suitable anchor point.** Don't waste time and energy securing a ground anchor if 'manual' methods will do the job. Winch-type recoveries can also be carried out with a hand-operated cable winch (Tirfor) or adapting a Hi-Lift Jack. See Section 3.I.

Your Land Rover must be equipped with a first aid kit and and fire extinguisher.

The first aid kit should be matched to the first aid skills of the user, so ensure maximum expert advice and training beforehand.

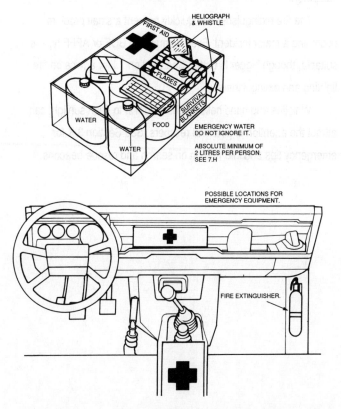

FIRST AID

HELIOGRAPH & WHISTLE

FLARES

SURVIVAL BLANKETS

WATER

FOOD

WATER

EMERGENCY WATER DO NOT IGNORE IT.

ABSOLUTE MINIMUM OF 2 LITRES PER PERSON. SEE 7.H

POSSIBLE LOCATIONS FOR EMERGENCY EQUIPMENT.

FIRE EXTINGUISHER.

Make sure it is easily accessible but packed in a strong box and located so that it is protected at the time it might be needed most - in an accident.

REMEMBER - Your first aid kit can save lives - keep it safe.

If your journeys are likely to take you into extremely remote regions, consider taking emergency food and water rations, blankets (cotton and heat-retaining 'space' blankets) and distress signal equipment.

The fire extinguisher can quickly prevent a small problem becoming a major incident. Even a small 1kg BCF or AFFF type is suitable, though bigger is better. See Section 7.I for advice on fire fighting and extinguishers.

Whistles and hand heliographs (mirrors) to flash sunlight can attract the attention of potential rescuers. See Section 3.K for emergency tips and information on search and rescue beacons.

A complete range of bolt-on extras which can further enhance the versatility of the Land Rover are available - nudge bars, roof racks, auxillary lighting are available from Land Rover Parts (See Section 1.G Optional Equipment and Accessories.)

In addition, highly specialised equipment - though officially unapproved by Land Rover - is available from specialist outlets.

1. ROLL – OVER CAGE - A specialist safety feature. Can be important for driving at speed over rough terrain.

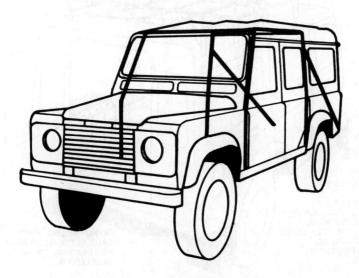

SEEK EXPERT ADVICE.

2. WATER/FUEL CARRIERS - Generally designed for external fitment to vehicle or roof rack. This saves interior space but opens up risk to accident damage, theft and - in the case of fuel containers - fire.

For water, use lightweight military-type containers which are proof against algae growth. Canvas or animal skin water bags lose contents through evaporation but keep water cool.

For fuel, always use metal containers.

FOR PROTECTION AGAINST SPILLS
WIRE LOCK JERRY-CAN CAPS CLOSED.

4 JERRY CANS ON
ROOF IS MAXIMUM
ROOF LOAD!

JERRY CANS INSIDE

IF CARRYING FUEL
(ESPECIALLY GASOLINE)
INSIDE, NO SMOKING,
KEEP WELL VENTILATED.
OPEN OUTSIDE AS
CANS MAY BE UNDER
PRESSURE.

DO NOT MOUNT JERRY
CANS AT FRONT OR REAR
FOR REASONS OF SAFETY
IN COLLISION.

NEVER FILL JERRY CANS MORE THAN 3/4 FULL (USUALLY 20 LITRES) AS COMPLETELY FULL CANS HAVE NO AIR SPACE FOR FUEL EXPANSION.

3. RADIO EQUIPMENT - A SW (Short Wave) radio is often the only way of keeping in touch with world news from Europe - and of hearing about local developments and conditions which may affect you.

For communications within a small fleet operation, the cheapness and short-range effectiveness of CB (Citizen's Band) radio may be adequate but it is more likely that a proper two-way radio system will be required - seek expert advice.

REMEMBER - **Many countries insist on special licences for two-way radios and often vehicles must not be imported with one fitted. Check local regulations.**

TO AVOID OFF ROAD DAMAGE DETACHABLE AERIAL BEST.

ALL TWO-WAY SETS MAY REQUIRE LICENSING IN COUNTRY OF OPERATION. SEEK EXPERT ADVICE.

OFTEN UNABLE TO IMPORT FITTED TO VEHICLE DUE TO SPECIAL LICENCE REQUIREMENT.

4. STEERING PROTECTION - A precaution which is recommended when a vehicle is to operate in rocky or wooded areas. Alloy
guards which are mounted direct to the chassis combine lightness
with strength.

**SOME DESIGNS CAN CAUSE AXLE OVERHEATING IN HOT
TERRITORIES. SEEK EXPERT ADVICE.**

5. COMPASS - Vehicle-mounted compasses can be disturbed by
the body metal and stray electrical signals from the vehicle. Opt for
a hand held compass used away from the vehicle.

6. G.P.S. - There are various modern G.P.S. instruments available,
of varying power. Consult a specialised supplier for advice as to
which will best suit your intended operations area.

7. AIR HORNS - The sound produced travels far beyond the distance covered by a standard horn - can be useful when competing
for space with lorries on narrow mountain roads!

8. SECURITY ALARMS - Local conditions may make the fitting of
an alarm advisable. A simple vehicle immobiliser switch in the ignition (petrol-engined vehicles) or in the fuel solenoid (diesel engines)
may be enough. For specialised systems, seek expert advice.

7. WHAT IF . . . . ?

7. WHAT IF. . .?

CONTENTS

7.A PHONETIC ALPHABET

Trying to spell an important word over a crackling telephone line or poor radio link can lead to mistakes. This phonetic alphabet is used by aircraft controllers and NATO forces and is thought to be the most common in international use.

A	–	Alpha	N	–	November
B	–	Bravo	O	–	Oscar
C	–	Charlie	P	–	Papa
D	–	Delta	Q	–	Quebec
E	–	Echo	R	–	Romeo
F	–	Foxtrot	S	–	Sierra
G	–	Golf	T	–	Tango
H	–	Hotel	U	–	Uniform
I	–	India	V	–	Victor
J	–	Juliet	W	–	Whisky
K	–	Kilo	X	–	X-ray
L	–	Lima	Y	–	Yankee
M	–	Mike	Z	–	Zulu

SIMPLE RADIO OPERATION

CALLING - (On call frequency) say the call sign of person you want and repeat, followed by your call sign and repeat, e.g. Foxtrot 2, Foxtrot 2, Alpha 1, Alpha 1. When contact made change frequency. At end of your part of conversation say "over". At finish of your call say your call sign then "out".

This standard has been laid down mainly for military aircraft pilots who have made a forced landing but is useful for a vehicle crew in trouble in a remote area. The standard below has been adapted where necessary to suit vehicle use.

Use the symbols sparingly to avoid confusing searchers. Make them as large as possible (up to 10 feet in length) and ensure they contrast with the ground as much as possible. A roll of fluorescent strip as used in perimeter marking is ideal. The alerted pilot should drop notes to confirm his sighting of you.

REQUIRE DOCTOR – SERIOUS INJURIES	I	WILL ATTEMPT TO START VEHICLE	▷
REQUIRE MEDICAL SUPPLIES	I I	VEHICLE SERIOUSLY DAMAGED	L⅂
UNABLE TO PROCEED (ON FOOT)	X	PROBABLY SAFE TO LAND HERE	△
REQUIRE FOOD AND WATER	F	REQUIRE FUEL AND OIL	L
REQUIRE FIREARMS AND AMMUNITION	V	ALL WELL	LL
REQUIRE MAP AND COMPASS	▢	NO	N
REQUIRE SIGNAL LAMP WITH BATTERY AND RADIO	¦	YES	Y
INDICATE DIRECTION TO PROCEED	K	NOT UNDERSTOOD	⅃L
AM PROCEEDING IN THIS DIRECTION	→	REQUIRE ENGINEER	W

VISUAL BODY SIGNALS

1. Affirmative (Yes).

   Wave cloth or hand up and down slowly with side of body towards aircraft.

2. Negative (No).

   Wave cloth or hand across body, facing aircraft.

3. Pick us up - vehicle abandoned.

   Hold arms above head to form a V.

   (Source: Tom Sheppard)

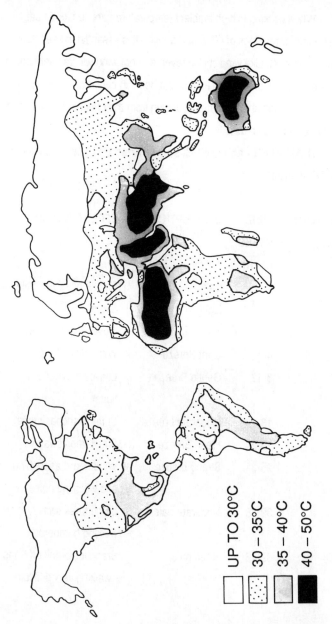

UP TO 30°C

30 – 35°C

35 – 40°C

40 – 50°C

7.D HIGH AMBIENT TEMPERATURES – WIND HEAT

When working in high ambient temperatures above blood heat - thermometer readings of 40°C and above - it is essential to keep your shirt on at least. Like wind chill in reverse, a hot wind will transfer heat to your bare skin more quickly than sweat helps to cool it.

Even a thin shirt insulates your skin from the effect of the wind and helps reduce water loss.

REMEMBER - Above 40°C, stay covered up to avoid wind heat and dehydration.

BEAUFORT NO.	WIND SPEED (MPH)	DESCRIPTION	EFFECT INLAND
O	0	Calm	Smoke rises vertically
1	1-3	Light Air	Slight movement of smoke
2	4-7	Light Breeze	Wind felt on face
3	8-12	Gentle Breeze	Leaves move, flags flutter
4	13-18	Moderate breeze	Small branches move
5	19-24	Fresh Breeze	Small trees sway
6	25-31	Strong breeze	Wind heard as rushing and whistling noise
7	32-38	Moderate gale	Large trees sway, walking hampered
8	39-46	Fresh gale	Branches break off trees - walking very difficult

9	47-54	Strong gale	Slates blown off roof
10	55-63	Whole gale	Trees down
11	64-75	Storm	Serious Damage
12	75+	Hurricane	Extensive Devastation

The strength of the sun's rays can be measured as heat at the Earth's surface in Watts per square metre. Solar load is much greater in desert area near the Equator than in Europe.

In practice, this means that any metal object left in the sun for a few minutes can burn you - including the bodywork of your Land Rover which can reach 107°C. Dark colours absorb heat - white reflects it.

To appreciate the power of the sun, it helps to think of a square metre as a small table and 1000 Watts as the heat given off by a single bar electric fire.

TYPICAL APPROXIMATE HIGHEST VALUES OF SOLAR LOAD (Watts per sq metre)

United Kingdom	200
Southern Spain	400
Sahara Desert	1100

Solar radiation (ultra-violet) can be reflected off surfaces like sand or water. **Always wear sun glasses to protect your eyes from the effects.**

As the air thins at altitude, the more of it the human body has to breathe. At 1000 metres above sea level, it needs 10 per cent more than at sea level.

Drive more slowly at altitude - it helps reduce the physical strain as well as the risk from hairpin bends!

Engines need air too - less air means reduced power at altitude – turbo-chargers help to maintain power.

Diesel injection pumps must be recalibrated by an expert to avoid over-fuelling (seen as black smoke) if the vehicle is to work for long periods at high altitudes. Petrol engines must be retuned.

REMEMBER - High altitude effects engine and human efficiency.

Don't forget that the higher you go the colder it becomes. Avoid diving into a stream or pool after a long hot drive up from the dusty plain below.

Cooking - unless you use a pressure cooker, water will take longer to boil. The effectiveness of your vehicle cooling system pressure cap also becomes increasingly important.

ALTITUDE* METRES	DENSITY KG/M³	%	AIR TEMPERATURE °C	BOILING POINT OF WATER (°C)
0	1.226	100	15.0	100
200	1.202	98	13.7	99
500	1.168	95	11.8	98
1000	1.112	91	8.5	97
2000	1.007	82	2.0	93
4000	0.819	67	-11.0	87

* Altitude shown above standard sea level

(Source: Bosch automotive handbook - Edition 1)

7.G PERCENTAGE HUMIDITY – WHAT DOES IT MEAN?

Humidity is a measurement of water content in the air. The maximum possible level of water content in the air increases with air temperature. Levels of humidity are quoted as a percentage of the maximum possible water content.

Example: If it is 30°C air temperature and the humidity is 20 gm/m^3 then 20 divided by 30.4 (see table below) multiplied by 100 = 66% humidity - not too unpleasant.

The closer to the sea you are, the higher the water content in the air and the longer it will take for sweat to evaporate. The bonus is that a Land Rover's cooling system works even more efficiently in higher humidity.

AIR TEMPERATURE °C	0	10	20	30	40	50
Max humidity gm/m^3	4.84	9.41	17.3	30.4	51.1	83

(Source: Bosch Automotive Handbook - Second Edition)

HIGH MEASURED VAPOUR CONCENTRATION WITH ASSOCIATED TEMPERATURE

Location	Maximum vapour concentration gm/m^3	Temperature Degrees C	Relative Humidity %
Bahrain	34	33	97
Aden	30	34	77
Karachi	29	32	85
Hong Kong	27	32	80
Darwin	27	32	80
Gan	26	31	81
Akrotiri	26	32	78
Cairo	20	32	59
Boscombe Down	18	29	64

(Source: Defence standard 00-35 part 4 issue 1 Nov 1986)

MAINTAINING YOUR WATER BALANCE

The hotter it becomes, the more you perspire to keep your temperature 'normal'. But you need to consume water if your own cooling system is to work effectively. The table below shows how much you need when simply resting out of the sun. The bigger you are, the harder you work, the more fluid you need. If in doubt, drink!

When working in high temperatures, Oral Rehydration Salts (ORS) will help maintain body salt level. ORS is available in powder form in sachets which you mix with water - it tastes like tears. Alternatively salts are mixed with glucose to make them taste sweeter.

MAX DAILY TEMPERATURE (°C)	43	38	33	<28
LITRES PER 24 HOURS PER MAN	5.3	2.4	1.2	1.0

DAYS OF EXPECTED SURVIVAL WITHOUT WATER

If you become stranded in a hot area the following is designed to help you calculate how long water will last, how much you should take on a journey which is likely to involve high temperatures, and how many days' survival is possible on a given amount of water.

For this purpose, 'survival' means that the person's condition towards the end of the period shown would be extremely serious.

WARNING - NEVER DRINK VEHICLE FLUIDS - THEY ARE TOXIC.

DAYS OF EXPECTED SURVIVAL WITHOUT WATER

HUMAN ACTIVITY	MAX DAILY SHADE TEMP (°C)	TOTAL WATER AVAILABLE PER MAN (Litres)					
		0	1	2	4	10	20
RESTING	50	2.5	2.5	2.5	3.0	3.5	4.5
IN SHADE	45	3.0	3.0	3.5	4.0	4.5	7.0
AT ALL	40	4.5	5.0	5.5	6.5	8.5	12.0
TIMES	35	7.0	8.0	8.5	10	14	20
	30	9.5	10.5	11.5	13	19	30
	25	11	12	13.5	15.5	22.5	34.5
	20	12	13	14	16.5	23.5	36.5
WALKING	50	1	2	2	2.5	3.5	–
ONLY AT		(40)	(40)	(48)	(56)	(64)	–
NIGHT AND	40	3	3.5	3.5	4	5	
RESTING IN		(40)	(40)	(48)	(56)	(72)	
SHADE BY	30	7	7.5	8.0	9.0	11.0	
DAY (Km		(65)	(70)	(78)	(100)	(112)	
walked shown	20	9.0	9.5	10.5	12.5	15.5	
in brackets)		(90)	(98)	(130)	(175)	(225)	

Based on RAF PAM (AIR) - DESERT SURVIVAL

(Source: Tom Sheppard - Desert Expeditions)

7.I FIRE FIGHTING

Prevention is better than cure; always keep your vehicle clean from dry grass strands and seeds, especially around electrical cables and hot engine areas, as well as the radiator. **IT IS ESPECIALLY IMPORTANT TO MAKE FREQUENT CHECKS UNDERNEATH ALONG THE LENGTH OF THE EXHAUST PIPE. GRASS IS VERY EASILY TRAPPED BETWEEN CHASSIS RAILS, GEARBOX AND EXHAUST, AND CAN RAPIDLY.IGNITE.**

Remember that it takes a cool head to tackle a fire. Make sure you know in advance what steps you need to take. If you know in advance what to do, you are more likely to react quickly, safely and correctly.

1. Get people and animals away from dangers without causing panic. If someone is on fire, lay them down to avoid flame inhalation before smothering the flames.

2. Assess the cause of the fire before you attempt to tackle it. Then decide on the most suitable substance to fight it. See the list overleaf. Remember that water can actually make matters worse or more dangerous.

3. If applicable, disconnect mains/bottled gas and electrical power supplies to building.

4. Don't take needless risks. If a blaze is out of control but unlikely to spread, it may be wiser to let it burn.

5. OIL AND FUEL FIRES - Never use water to put out flammable liquids. The water will turn to steam (gas) and will carry the flames upwards.

6. PRESSURISED BOTTLES - There is a real danger of explosion from bottles containing butane, propane, oxygen, compressed air or welding gas which are under heat. Move bottles away only if this can be done without risk. If bottles are close to source of fire, evacuate people and animals to a safe distance.

7. ELECTRICAL FIRES - Never use water or foam to extinguish an electrical fire. They may conduct electric shocks.

FIRE EXTINGUISHER COLOUR CODING

There is no internationally agreed standard for identifying extinguisher types but most countries use the following colours to identify types (whole exterior colour or 'spot' colour)

RED - Water/Carbon Dioxide - Soda Acid Type

Use on: Wood, Paper, Textiles

Never use on: Electrical fires or flammable liquids

WHITE - Water-based foam

Use on: Wood, Paper, Textiles, Flammable liquids, low voltage fires

Never use on: High voltage fires

CREAM - Foam

Use on: Flammable liquids

Never use on: Electrical fires

BLUE - Dry powder

Use on: Flammable liquids and electrical fires up to 1000 volts

Never use on: Very high voltage electrical fires

BLACK - Carbon dioxide gas

Use on: Flammable liquids and high voltage electrical fires

GREEN - Vapourising liquids (bcf)

Use on: Flammable liquids and high voltages

WARNING - Blue, Black and Green extinguishers will put out flames but do not quench (cool) hot material. Fire may flare up again so monitor until material has cooled below flash point.

TIPS:

Sand and earth are effective for smothering flames but only when dry.

Vehicle fires can be treated with any extinguisher because of the low voltages involved but do not use water. Do not use red extinguishers on fuel/oil fires.

This data is useful when you need to convert units. e.g. A generator you want to transport is marked as weighing 700 lb, your Station Wagon payload is 1287 kg. Under the weight section of the table in the pounds column you find 1 pound = 0.454 kg. Therefore 700 x 0.454 = 318 kg – so you are alright if carrying it without other heavy items

LENGTH

METRE	KILOMETER	INCH	FOOT	YARD	MILE
1	0.001	39.37	3.28	1.09	0.00062
1000	1	39370	3281	1094	0.62
0.0254	0.00003	1	0.083	0.028	0.00002
0.3048	0.0003	12	1	0.33	0.00019
0.914	0.00091	36	3	1	0.00057
1609	1.609	63360	5280	1760	1

AREA

SQUARE METRE	HECTARE	SQUARE KILOMETRE	SQUARE YARD	ACRE
1	0.0001	–	1.196	0.00025
10000	1	0.01	11960	2.47
–	100	1	–	247
0.836	0.00004	–	1	0.00021
4047	0.405	0.00405	4840	1

VOLUME

CUBIC METRE	LITRE	US GALLON	CUBIC INCH	CUBIC FOOT	IMPERIAL PINT	IMPERIAL GALLON
1	1000	264	61024	35.31	1760	220
0.001	1	0.264	61	0.035	1.79	0.22
0.0038	3.785	1	231	0.134	6.64	0.83
0.00002	0.0164	0.0043	1	0.0006	0.029	0.0036
0.028	28.32	7.48	1728	1	49.84	6.23
0.00057	0.568	0.150	34.68	0.02	1	0.125
0.0046	4.55	1.2	277	0.161	8	1

PINT (US) = 0.473 LITRES (17% LESS THAN UK PINT)

WEIGHT

GRAM	KILOGRAM	TONNE	OUNCE	POUND	STONE	CWT (UK)	TON (UK)
1	0.001	–	0.035	0.0022	0.00016	–	–
1000	1	0.001	35.27	2.2	0.157	0.02	0.001
–	1000	1	35274	2201	157.5	19.7	0.984
28.35	0.028	–	1	0.0625	0.0045	–	–
454	0.454	–	16	1	0.071	0.0006	–
6350	6.35	0.006	224	14	1	0.125	0.0063
50802	50.8	0.051	1792	112	8	1	0.05
–	1016	1.02	35840	2240	160	20	1

CWT (US) = 100 LB
TON (US) = 2000 LB (ABOUT 10% LESS THAN TON (UK) OR TONNE)

If you need to establish the weight of an object, this table will help you work it out approximately.

Estimate the object's volume - say, 30 litres. If it is iron, you can calculate 30 x 7.87 = 236 Kgs. In other words, the weight of three adult passengers.

SOLIDS

Aluminium	2.70
Asphalt	1.1 to 1.4
Brass	8.4
Brick	>1.9
Bronze	8.8
Chalk	1.8 to 2.6
Charcoal	0.3 to 0.5
Concrete	1.8 to 2.2
Copper	8.93
Cork	0.1 to 0.3
Clay (Dry)	1.5 to 1.8
Ice	0.92
Iron	7.87
Iron (Cast)	7.25
Glass	2.4 to 2.7
Granite	2.7
Lead	11.3
Leather	0.86 to 1.0
Magnesium Alloys	1.8
Marble	2.6 to 2.8
Mortar	1.6 to 1.8
Paper	0.7 to 1.2
Paraffin	0.9

Plastic Rigid Foam	0.015 to 0.06
Plastic Thermoset	1.3 to 1.8
PVC	1.4
Roofing Felt	1.1
Rubber	1.08
Rubber (Hard)	1.2 to 1.5
Sand (Dry)	1.5 to 1.7
Steel	7.9 to 8.7
Tin	7.28
Wax	0.96
Wood	0.5 to 0.72

LIQUIDS

Alcohol	0.79
Anti-Freeze	1.114
Battery Acid	1.28
Diesel Fuel	0.86
Gasoline	0.78
Linseed Oil	0.93
Lubricating Oil	0.91
Kerosene	0.76 to 0.86
Silicone Oil (WD40)	0.76 to 0.98
Water	1.00

(source - Bosch Automotive handbook)

7.L TEMPERATURE CONVERSION SCALE

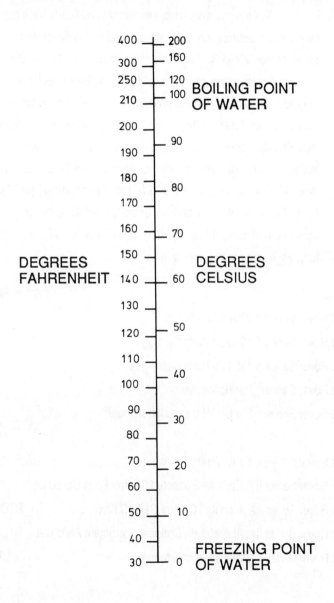

DEGREES FAHRENHEIT		DEGREES CELSIUS
400	200	
300	160	
250	120	
210	100	BOILING POINT OF WATER
200		
190	90	
180	80	
170		
160	70	
150		
140	60	
130		
120	50	
110		
100	40	
90	30	
80		
70	20	
60		
50	10	
40		
30	0	FREEZING POINT OF WATER

7.M LAND ROVER PUBLICATIONS

To help you work more effectively Land Rover have published many technical books to assist in the maintenance and repair of their vehicles. For manuals and other titles for vehicles currently in production consult your local Land Rover dealer or refer to their website www.landrover.com. For out of production vehicles Land Rover Heritage have appointed Brooklands Books to look after the needs of owners of older vehicles. Currently the following manuals etc. are available from Brooklands Books Ltd. PO Box 146, Cobham, Surrey, KT11 1LG, UK. Telephone: 44 (0) 1932 865051 Fax: 44 (0) 1932 868893 email: sales@brooklands-books.com or consult their website: www.brooklands-books.com for a list of their latest publications.

TITLE	PART No.
Land Rover Series 1 Workshop Manual	4291
Land Rover Series 1 1948-53 Parts Catalogue	4051
Land Rover Series 1 1954-58 Parts Catalogue	4107
Land Rover Series 1 Instruction Manual	4277
Land Rover Series 1 & II Diesel Instruction Manual	4343
Land Rover Series II & IIA Workshop Manual	AKM8159
Land Rover Series II & Early IIA Bonneted Control Parts Catalogue	605957
Land Rover Series IIA Bonneted Control Parts Catalogue	RTC9840CC
Land Rover Series IIA, III & 109 V8 Optional Equipment Parts Cat.	RTC9842CE
Land Rover Series IIA/IIB Instruction Manual	LSM64 IM

Land Rover Series III Workshop Manual   AKM3648

Land Rover Series III Workshop Manual V8 Supplement (edn. 2)   AKM8022

Land Rover Series III 88, 109 & 109 V8 Parts Catalogue   RTC9841CE

Land Rover Series III Owners Manual 1971-81   607324B

Land Rover Series III Owners Manual 1981-85   AKM8155

Land Rover 90/110 & Defender Workshop Manual 1983-92   SLR621ENWM

Land Rover Defender Workshop Manual 1993-95   LDAWMEN93

Land Rover Defender 300 Tdi & Supplements WM 1996-98   LRL 0097 ENG BB

Land Rover Defender Td5 W'ks Man. & Supplements 1999-2006   LRL 0410BB

Land Rover Defender Elect. Man. Td5 1999-06 & 300Tdi 2002-06   LRD5EHBB

Land Rover 110 Parts Catalogue 1983-86   RTC9863CE

Land Rover Defender Parts Catalogue 1987-2006   STC9021CC

Land Rover 90 • 110 Owners Handbook 1983-1990   LSM0054

Land Rover 90 • 110 • 130 Owners Handbook 1991-Feb. 1994   LHAHBEN93

Land Rover 90 • 110 • 130 Owners Handbook March 1994-1998   LRL 0087ENG/2

Discovery W'ks Man. 1990-94 (petrol 3.5, 3.9, Mpi & diesel 200 Tdi)   SJR900ENWM

Discovery W'ks Man. 1995-98 (ptrl 2.0 Mpi, 3.9, 4.0 V8 & diesel 300 Tdi)   LRL 0079BB

Discovery Series II W'ks Man. 1999-02 (petrol 4.0 V8 & diesel Td5)   VDR 100090

Discovery Prts Cat. 1989-98 (2.0 Mpi, 3.5, 3.9 V8 & 200 Tdi & 300 Tdi)   RTC9947CF

Discovery Owners Hbk 1990-1991 (petrol 3.5 & diesel 200 Tdi)   SJR820ENHB90

Freelander Workshop Manual 1998-2000 (petrol 1.8 and diesel 2.0)   LRL 0144

Land Rover Military (Lightweight) Series III Parts Catalogue

Land Rover Military (Lightweight) Series III User Manual   608180

Land Rover 101 1 Tonne Forward Control Workshop Manual   RTC9120

Land Rover 101 1 Tonne Forward Control Parts Catalogue   608294B

Land Rover 101 1 Tonne Forward Control User Manual   608239

Range Rover Workshop Manual 1970-85 (petrol 3.5)   AKM3630

Range Rover Workshop Manual 1986-89   SRR660ENWM &

(petrol 3.5 & diesel 2.4 Turbo VM)   LSM180WS4 Ed 2

Range Rover Workshop Manual 1990-94

(petrol 3.9, 4.2 & diesel 2.5 Turbo VM, 200 Tdi)   LHAWMENA02

Range Rover Wrks Man. 1995-01 (ptrl 4.0, 4.6 & BMW 2.5 diesel)   LRL 0326ENG BB

Range Rover Parts Catalogue 1970-85 (petrol 3.5)   RTC9846CH

Range Rover Parts Catalogue 1986-91

(petrol 3.5, 3.9 & diesel 2.4 Turbo VM & 2.5 Turbo VM)   RTC9908CB

Range Rover Parts Catalogue 1992-94 MY & 95 MY Classic

(petrol 3.9, 4.2 & diesel 2.5 Turbo VM, 200 Tdi & 300 Tdi)   RTC9961CB

Range Rover Owners Handbook 1970-80 (petrol 3.5)   606917

Range Rover Owners Handbook 1981-82 (petrol 3.5)   AKM 8139

Range Rover Owners Handbook 1983-85 (petrol 3.5)   LSM 0001HB

Range Rover Owners Hbk 1986-87 (petrol 3.5 & diesel 2.4 Turbo VM)   LSM 129HB

Range Rover Owners Hbk 1988-89 (petrol 3.5 & diesel 2.4 Turbo VM)   SRR600ENHB

Engine Overhaul Manuals for Land Rover & Range Rover

300 Tdi Engine, R380 Manual Gearbox &   LRL 003, 070 & 081

LT230T Transfer Gearbox Overhaul Manuals

Petrol Engine V8 3.5, 3.9, 4.0, 4.2 & 4.6 Overhaul Manuals   LRL 004 & 164

Land Rover/Range Rover Driving Techniques   LR 369

Working in the Wild - Manual for Africa   SMR 684MI

Workshop Manual Owners Edition

Land Rover 2 / 2A / 3 Owners Workshop Manual 1959-1983

Land Rover 90, 110 & Defender Workshop Manual Owners Edition 1983-1995

Land Rover Discovery Workshop Manual Owners Edition 1990-1998

Land Rover Defender 200 & 300 Tdi Workshop Manual Owners Ed. 1990-1998

Land Rover Defender Td5 Workshop Manual Owners Edition 1998-2006

7.N INDEPENDENT PUBLICATIONS

There are literally hundreds of books that might be of interest with regard to readers of this publication and any list given here would soon become out of date. The best and most useful guide regarding available books can be found on Amazon's website: www.amazon.com.

A range of books that will be of interest to Land Rover owners is the Brooklands 'road test' series which cover virtually all of their models, except the Freelander. These books provide a full and wide-ranging collection of road tests, comparison tests, new model descriptions, long-term tests and other articles taken from the world's leading motoring magazines. Filled with informed and reliable test comment, these books furnish all the essential information on most Land Rovers.

LAND ROVER SERIES ONE 1948-1958. The Land Rover was conceived after the second war for overseas and agricultural use and was designed to use as many of the company's existing components as possible. It was panelled with aluminium alloy and they were first displayed at the Amsterdam Motor Show. Intended to be a stop-gap it proved so popular that they are still in production over 50 years later. This is a book of road tests, specifications etc. and follows its development over the first decade. 100 pages, 250 illus. Soft Bound. Ref. A-LR4810   (ISBN 185520 0805)

LAND ROVER SERIES II & IIa 1958-1971. Ten years after the introduction of the first Land Rovers came the Series II. This had a much rounder body and more conveniently placed instruments. The 107in wheelbase Station Wagon was replaced by the 88in and 109in versions and fitted with both petrol and diesel engines. Seats became more comfortable and the de luxe model was trimmed and carpeted. The Series IIa was heralded by a change of engine size to 2.25 litres. A forward-control model was introduced in 1962 and a 110in model in 1966 with better stability. In 1968 the headlamps were moved from the grille to the wings for some overseas markets and a 1-ton version of the 109in model was introduced. The headlamps were moved into the wings on all models in 1969. This is a book of contemporary road tests, technical and service data, driver's impressions, used car tests, off-road and optional equipment reports. Models covered include: 88, 109, 2.25, Station Wagon, Fire Appliance, Motor Caravan, 6-cyl. LWB, 2.6 Estate, Sandtrekker, LtWt V8, Forward Control. 100 pages, 250 illus. Soft Bound. Ref. A-LR58 (ISBN 094820 7981)

LAND ROVER SERIES III 4X4 PERFORMANCE PORTFOLIO 1971-1985.
The second major face-lift in the life of the Land Rover was introduced with the Series III model in 1971. Production figures cannot be confirmed but it is thought that around 440,000 were built between 1971 and 1985. As this was a bad time for British Leyland most of the profits went into the car division and few changes were made. Even when Land Rover became a separate operating division in 1978 it took until 1983 for a replacement to be produced. Not every market took to the new vehicles so the Series III remained in low volume production until 1985. This is a book of contemporary road and comparison tests, specifications and technical data, off-road reports, long terms tests, 'driver's reports', plus advice on buying a used example. Types covered include: 4 & 6-cylinder, 2.6 station wagon,

SWB, V8, LWB, Diesel, Pick-up, 3/4 ton, 3S Station Wagon, 3-9D, County. 140 pages, 350 illus. Soft Bound. Ref. A-LR71PP (ISBN 185520 4762)

LAND ROVER 90, 110, DEFENDER GOLD PORTFOLIO 1983-1994. By the end of the 1970s lack of investment meant that the marque was now outdated. The introduction of the 110 in 1983 with improved suspension and more luxury was long overdue. The short-wheelbase 90 came just over a year later. These new models were aimed at the higher end of the market. Sales were steady due to longevity and reliability and the Defender replaced the 90 and 110 models in 1990. The Defender had the option of the 200Tdi diesel engine and had power assisted steering. This is a book of contemporary road tests, technical data and specifications, with off-road reports, background information and driving impressions. Models covered include: County Station Wagon, V8, Diesel, County TD, Amphi-Rover, Automatic, Defender 90, 110, 110 Hiline SW, Turbo D 110, Defender 130 Tipper, Tdi, Defender County, Military. 172 pages, 400 illus. Soft Bound. Ref. A-LR83GP (ISBN 18552 2530)

LAND ROVER DISCOVERY 4X4 PERFORMANCE PORTFOLIO 1989-2000. There are three distinct phases of the Discovery. The first (1989-1994) were characterised by square headlights and, in diesel form, the 200 Tdi engine. The second (1994-1998) had rectangular lights and, in diesel form, the 300Tdi engine. Since 1998 there has been a redesigned Series II vehicle which can be had with the Td5 diesel engine. The V8 petrol engine has been available since the beginning and has gone through various guises and between 1992 and 1996 there was a 4-cylinder petrol option though this was never a strong seller. The most popular models have always been the diesels. The diesel has also made the Discovery into an off-roader's delight. This is a book of contemporary road and comparison tests, technical data and specifications, new model introductions, long term tests, driver's impressions, and contains a 'buyer's guide' for those looking for a used example. 140 pages, 400 illus. Soft Bound. Ref. A-LR89PP (ISBN 185520 5599)

7.0 ACKNOWLEDGEMENTS

Bill Treneman and Kirt Carolan, the authors, would like to thank all those below for their valuable help and advice during the production of this book. Without their support this book would not have been possible.

We would especially like to thank all the field workers of Oxfam, Save The Children, GOAL, UN High Commission for Refugees, UN World Food Programme, Saudi Red Crescent and German Agro-Action who made us so welcome during our stay in El Geneina, Sudan, during 1986.

KEN BAND, Reeves Green Partners Ltd - for breathing life into the final copy.

BRITISH ARMY - Special Tools Group.

BRITISH ARMY - 11 Maintenance Advisory Group.

MARTIN BETTERSLEY, Oxfam - Dessi Workshop, Ethiopia.

STEPHEN BRISTOW, SOS Sahel - Sudan Field Director.

ISABEL CARTER - Bishops Burton College of Agriculture.

GEORGE FENTON, Save The Children Fund - Sudan transport.

DICK FRANCIS, Land Rover - For his guidance and vision.

JIM HOWARD, Oxfam Technical Unit - For our secondment to Sudan.

ROBERT McADAM - Register of Engineers for Disaster Relief.

BILL MORRIS, Land Rover - For his support during this long project.

JACK MUGGERIDGE - Register of Engineers for Disaster Relief.

OXFAM - At Oxford and Overseas.

DAVID PANTON, Land Rover - for his support and encouragement.

MIKE PRIESTLY - Esso Research, Abingdon.

MIKE PRING, Save The Children Fund - Sudan and Ethiopia.

BERT RAMSDEN - Esso Research, Abingdon.

SIMON RANKIN, Land Rover - for the illustrations.

PETER RANGER - Register of Engineers for Disaster Relief.

CHRIS SCAIFE, Land Rover - for the cartoons.

TOM SHEPPARD MBE, Royal Geographical Society - Desert driving and survival advice.

KEN & JULIE SLAVIN, Quest 80 - Expedition advisors.

DEREK WEBB - Register of Engineers for Disaster Relief.

MIKE WHITWORTH - BP International.

NIGEL & SHANE WINSER - Royal Geographical Society.

New Revised Edition

We are indebted to Christopher Race for revising and editing this new edition. Christopher was born and raised in Africa. He has driven and maintained Land Rovers in Africa since 1955 and is currently head of a specialised safari company, Africa Insight (Pty) Ltd, in Botswana, operating Land Rovers in some of the wildest regions of the Continent. He also writes regularly for Land Rover Enthusiast Magazine and is an authority on travel and vehicle maintenance in Africa.

7.P ALPHABETICAL INDEX

Land Rover Restoration

Land Rover Restoration Portfolio

Land Rover Series I Restoration

Step-by-step reports on restoring a SWB Land Rover plus 'how to' info on dropping in a V8 or a 300 Tdi engine, overhauling brakes, axles, heater, propshaft and gearbox. Covered are pieces on towing, tracking, winching, cylinder head conversion plus advice on electrical and transfer box trouble-shooting. A comprehensive guide is included on how to buy a good secondhand Land Rover. 130 pages, 550 illustrations some in colour.

Practical Classics - The complete DIY Series I Land Rover restoration guide. Covering: engine, suspension, brakes, gearbox, carburation, body removal & replacement, electrics, chassis, doors & bulkhead repair & painting. Plus expert advice on buying a good used Land Rover. 92 pages, 11 in colour & over 580 black and white illustrations.

From specialist booksellers or, in case of difficulty, direct from the distributors:

Brooklands Books Ltd., PO Box 146, Cobham, Surrey, KT11 1LG, England.
Phone: 01932 865051   Fax: 01932 868803
E-Mail: sales@brooklands-books.com www.brooklands-books.com
Brooklands Books Australia, 3/37-39 Green Street, Banksmeadow, NSW 2019, Australia.
Telephone: 2 9695 7055   Fax: 2 9695 7355
CarTech, 39966 Grand Avenue, North Branch, MN 55056, USA.
Phone: 800 551 4754 & 651 277 1200   Fax: 651 277 1203
Motorbooks International, P.O. Box 1, Osceola, Wisconsin 54020, USA.
Phone: 800 826 6600 & 715 294 3345

www.brooklands-books.com

Land Rover Military

Combat Land Rovers Portfolio No.1

Land Rover Military Portfolio

Many articles cover the Wolf as it was introduced to the forces in all its guises. Included WMIK equipped Wolves in Sierra Leone, SOVs serving with the US Rangers, Desert Patrol Vehicles, CAVs. APVs, RAF 127s, 130s & 110 FFRs. 136 pages, 300 illus including 48 pages of colour. Soft Bound

Our previous book Land Rovers in Military Service, is now out of print and we have replaced it with this enlarged updated title. A Collection of 52 Military Scene features by Bob Morrison from Land Rover Owner magazine. 140 pages with colour. Soft Bound.

Land Rover

LAND ROVER
SERIES I · II & IIA
Gold Portfolio

1948-1971
80 · 86 · 107 · 88 · 109
Petrol and Diesel
4 and 6 cylinder

LAND ROVER
SERIES III
4 X 4 PERFORMANCE PORTFOLIO
1971-1985

Road tests   New model introductions   Performance data
Buying used   Touring   Specifications   Customising
Pick-up   Wagon   Hard top   Safari   4 & 6 cyl   V8   Diesel

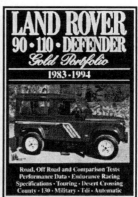

LAND ROVER
90 · 110 · DEFENDER
Gold Portfolio
1983-1994

Road, Off Road and Comparison Tests
Performance Data · Endurance Racing
Specifications · Touring · Desert Crossing
County · 130 · Military · Tdi · Automatic

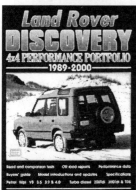

Land Rover
DISCOVERY
4x4 PERFORMANCE PORTFOLIO
1989-2000

Road and comparison tests   Off road reports   Performance data
Buyers' guide   Model introductions and updates   Specifications
Petrol Mpi   V8   3.5   3.9 & 4.0   Turbo diesel   200Tdi   300Tdi & TD5

COMBAT LAND ROVERS
LRM Portfolio No.1
by Bob Morrison

RANGE ROVER
Gold Portfolio
1970-1985

Road Tests · New Model Introductions
Long Term and Off Road Reports · Updates
Performance Data · History · Buying Used
Vogue · Janspeed · Schuler · Automatic

RANGE ROVER
Gold Portfolio
1985-1995

Road and comparison tests   Touring   Specifications
Technical and performance data   Model introductions
Long term reports   Janspeed   Highline   Buying used
County   Vogue   Tdi   EFi   LSE   SE   CSK   LWB

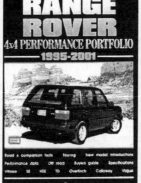

RANGE ROVER
4x4 PERFORMANCE PORTFOLIO
1995-2001

Road & comparison tests   Touring   New model introductions
Performance data   Off road   Buyers guide   Specifications
Vitesse   SE   HSE   TD   Overfinch   Callaway   Vogue

RANGE ROVER
TAKES ON THE COMPETITION